SICK &
TIRED
of being
F·A·T

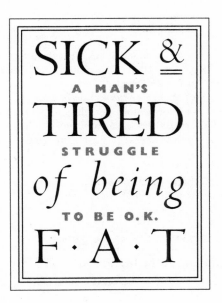

SICK &
A MAN'S
TIRED
STRUGGLE
of being
TO BE O.K.
F·A·T

ELIOT ALEXANDER

A Hazelden Book
HarperCollins*Publishers*

This edition is printed on acid-free paper that meets the American
National Standards Institute Z39.48 Standards.

FIRST HARPERCOLLINS EDITION PUBLISHED IN 1991.

Library of Congress Cataloging-in-Publication Data

Alexander, Eliot.
    Sick and tired of being fat : one man's struggle to be O.K. / Eliot
Alexander. — 1st HarperCollins ed.
        p.   cm.
    "A Hazelden book."
    ISBN 0–06–255353–4
    1. Alexander, Eliot—Mental health.   2. Compulsive eaters—United
States—Biography.   I. Title.
RC552.C65A44   1991
616.85'26—dc20
    [B]   90-55376
                                                                          CIP

91   92   93   94   95   CWI   10   9   8   7   6   5   4   3   2   1

Contents

PROLOGUE

*I have been overweight every
one of my forty-seven years.*

Dick warmly greeted Alan—my business partner—and me. A decade ago, he and Alan had shared an office as young hotshots who struggled and triumphed together in launching a new advertising agency in Chicago. I had met Dick in passing a couple of times before. Now, Alan and I had driven to his midtown Manhattan office to discuss a major new business venture with one of his key clients.

Dick ushered us into the spacious, elegantly furnished office he occupies as president of a large, multinational ad agency. He stood back and sized up Alan. What he saw was a man who takes fantastically—fanatically—good care of himself. Standing five-ten, weighing exactly 147 pounds, lean and taut and muscular as a greyhound, athletic and graceful, vegetarian, disciplined, Alan is an admirable physical specimen. But lately his five-mile-per-day running regimen had given him a look that went beyond lean to gaunt, prompting Dick to remark "Say, you look like you've lost a lot of weight—I mean, really a lot."

Then he glanced my way and saw a man who is thirty or forty pounds overweight, a man who despite regular running and tennis has a protruding stomach, bulging hips, and a puffy double chin. He added, in a tone of superiority and contempt, "And you, Eliot, look like you've put on everything he lost."

■ ■ ■

What does it mean to live inside a body that invites such a piercing insult? What does it mean to live inside a body that prompts a supposedly civilized man to be so rude? What is it about being overweight that allows near-strangers to casually trample your self-esteem?

I have been mentally answering that cruel son of a bitch every hour for three weeks now. I have told him I am astonished at his insensitivity. I have chewed him out for violating common courtesy. I have invented a hundred—no, a thousand—sarcastic replies designed to really hurt him, to pay him back with interest for the pain he made me feel. I have hated him with a black fury quite unlike anything I have ever felt before.

But it is no use.

I am stuck with him and with a world of people like him. This is a world in which fat is fair game. Anyone with a pair of eyes can spot flab, and that is apparently all it takes to trigger the emotional rape.

Dick's humiliating comment was the last straw for me. It set off something in me that said I had to take action about my fat once and for all. Perhaps you have had the same kind of experience, when you realized that people like Dick were never going to change and that it was up to you to find *some* way to defend yourself against their antifat prejudice.

I knew beyond a doubt that I had only two choices if I were to avoid that kind of pain in the future. Either I must lose the weight and keep it off, or I finally had to accept myself as a fat person who can't help being fat but who can learn how to forgive people like Dick for their ignorance and cruelty.

And that's what this book is about. It is the record of my eighteen-month experiment either to permanently change my appearance or to live as a fat man without regret, shame, or apology.

This book is *not* about dieting. You and I have both had quite enough failure at dieting. This book is about eating. About the way people like you and me eat. And about why we eat the way we do.

This book is about trying to escape the lonely hell of compulsive overeating. *Compulsive overeating* may be a new term to you. It was new to me just a couple of years ago when, after nearly fifty years of sneaky snacking and yo-yo dieting, my uncontrolled eating was leading me to an early grave. All the signs were there: my blood pressure was rising like a rocket, and my desire to live was falling like a stone. It took no great imagination to see that my steady weight gain of eight to ten pounds per year would put 250 to 300 pounds on my five-feet ten-inch frame in just a few more years. From there, my body's systems were sure to collapse through stroke, heart attack, circulatory problems, leg and joint breakdown, and the rest. My dad died early of all that stuff, and I had every reason to believe I would too. Worse, in the meantime, my very life was likely to collapse in a heap of despair and shame.

Over the years I had become desperate. I knew I had to do *something*. But I had already tried virtually everything—Weight Watchers, Diet Center, Golden Door vegetarianism, powders and pills, and every fad diet and "revolutionary" new book published during the past twenty-five years. God knows I was a world champion dieter and probably a highly valued customer of the commercial weight-loss industry. But they all failed. Every effort had failed: short-term loss, followed inevitably by the steady march back up again. All accompanied by the dark damnation of self-hatred, always cursing and beating myself up for my lack of willpower.

My self-hatred has been particularly terrible to live with. Here I am, a reasonably decent citizen who loves his family, pays his taxes, tells clerks when they give him too much change, conducts business generously—and lies, cheats, and steals to stuff himself with food. I have eaten more food away from the table—standing in the kitchen, sitting in the bathroom, parked in my car—than I have eaten at the table during my lifetime. I have devised a hundred ways to swipe food from jars and trays and containers to make it appear that nothing was taken. Me! A fairly nice guy!

I have felt real despair about controlling the demon that turns me into such a dishonest monster when it comes to food. In fact, although I am a life-loving person and would never end my own life, the only thoughts of suicide I ever had would come in the aftermath of an eating binge, when I felt like such a total shit.

I hated failing to control my eating because I hated being fat. But I hated it all the more for another reason: at least a handful of lifelong fat people do eventually beat the problem. The literature suggests that something like one in every twenty chronically fat people eventually succeeds in losing a significant amount of weight and keeping it off. So I knew it wasn't impossible—just very, very difficult.

The infuriating experience with Dick's stupid insult finally compelled me to put myself to the ultimate test. I'm a fairly competitive guy and couldn't stand the thought that some people out there could dig deep for the ability—the willpower—to succeed at this, when I couldn't. For one thing, I didn't like the thought that there was something I couldn't do. For another, I had to settle the question of whether fatness was my fate or just the result of my failure to deal with it.

So I determined to make one last effort, which I thought of as an experiment. This would be my all-out push, once and for all. I would give it everything. At the end, either I would be slim or I would know *for sure* that it was *impossible* for me to get there. I would leave no room for a voice to whisper inside me, *Well, Eliot, you just didn't try hard enough.*

The way I reach for the best in me is through writing. That is how I get most deeply in touch with my own feelings, thoughts, discoveries, alternatives, and possibilities. I decided that the best way to give the experiment everything I had was to write about it as I went along.

And so I did. During a major part of my once-and-for-all, I got up every morning about five-thirty to write for an hour or two before leaving for the office. This was my first entry:

Today is August 15 and I weigh 203½ pounds.

Today is the official start of my experiment. Today is the day I take one last run at transforming myself from a fat person to a trim person, and try to understand along the way why the effort is—or is not—working. As I sit here today, I weigh 203½, with a rich roll of flab hanging over my belt and a couple of breasts that would look better on a fifteen-year-old girl. I suppose I should weigh something more like 160, and getting there—or giving up on getting there and conceding that I am fat forever—will mark the end of this experiment.

I have no idea how this is going to turn out. But I am going to write about it every day until I conclude the experiment is over—until it is clearly settled one way or the other. Writing is the best way I have of learning what I am thinking and feeling, and that is central to the process. Damn it, I want to *understand* this stupid condition. I will stop when I am at peace with the verdict, once and for all.

Although I will try to keep a sense of humor about all of this, the issue is deadly serious. The pounds of fat on my body have been a source of self-loathing, public humiliation, and despair for me all my life. This is no laughing matter. The very subject triggers in me feelings of bitterness, rage, resentment, defensiveness, combativeness—and envy and longing.

How can I look at a magazine ad or TV commercial without being reminded, once again, what kind of men are considered attractive? Guys with no hips, flat bellies that ripple with muscles like a washboard, and taut thighs that don't chafe. Guys with sunken cheeks and jawlines that look chiseled from stone. Guys with visible Adam's apples.

Guys who are nothing like me at all.

I'm not one of those men and I never have been. In fact, I have always resented the hell out of men who got that kind of body when I didn't. I don't even know whether I *want* to be like them.

They and I are worlds apart. I have been overweight for every one of my forty-seven years. I have a lifetime of embarrassment, hurt feelings, yearning, and failures stuffed into the condition. My struggle now is to dig out this stuff, unbury it. Unbury it and follow wherever I am led. My fantasy is that it will lead me to be the one person in twenty who successfully sheds the fat and leaves it permanently behind.

But if it doesn't, by God, I will know the reason why.

And so, with great resolve, my quest began. What follows is what happened.

I

Maybe I know that I need help.

Today is August 16 and I weigh 205 pounds this morning.

I had planned to begin the weight-loss part of my experiment yesterday, but I didn't.

I spent the time gaining weight instead. About a pound and a half, to be exact. That was the result of a museum trip with my family to New York City. The museum never laid a glove on me. But at a restaurant called Summerhouse, I managed to down broiled red pepper and mozzarella cheese; rotini pasta with a chardonnay sauce riddled with both clams and snails; biscuits as flaky and buttery as shortbread, spread with strawberry butter; and a raspberry/blackberry torte that was, we all agreed, one of the most exquisite desserts we had ever tasted.

If a person has already decided to throw in the towel and stay flabby, Summerhouse should definitely be the first stop. I have not yet decided to throw in the towel. That makes my pigging out at Summerhouse all the more vexing. Here I am on the very day I intended to begin my Great Experiment, and I blow it. What's going on, anyhow? Was I mistaken in concluding that the time has come? Do I deny that my eating habits must now change for the rest of my life?

It is the lifetime-change aspect that is so daunting. I know from past experience that I can lose weight. I have lost several hundred pounds during my previous diets. That's *almost* easy.

What is not easy is keeping it off. I have always gained it back, and usually a couple of more pounds as well. Which, in turn, makes each subsequent taking-it-off that much harder. It is so futile. Why bother? Who wants to go through predictable defeat when it can be avoided? What I am looking for is a predictable victory, and it's nowhere in sight.

These days my eye is more readily caught by articles about weight. In this week's *New York Times Magazine*, there are two: James Michener apologizing for the early death by heart attack of the father of American recreational running, Jim Fixx; and another (in the beauty section, naturally) mentioning the futility of short-term diets and the necessity for life-long behavioral change.

I am all too aware that my extra pounds constitute a health hazard, and common sense would prompt me to lose them just to give me better odds of living a long time. I did not inherit a wonderful biological track record on heart and blood pressure risks; as I mentioned before, my dad died early of cardiovascular problems, and so did his parents. I know being free of fat would help offset any risky predispositions. Fixx lost sixty-one pounds and, as Michener would have it, probably added a decade or more to an otherwise even shorter life expectancy.

I am no dummy. I do not lack common sense. And I am decidedly not a suicidal type. Yet I do not do what is clearly in my best interest. Why?

Why?

I will not end this experiment until I understand the answer to that question. I may not like the answer I reach, but I will reach it.

One spur to my motivation is the galling example set by people who are successful at losing weight and keeping it off. Fixx is one example; Jack Nicklaus is another. Misery loves company, and when I was younger, I used to comfort myself with the sight of a fairly chubby Nicklaus winning everything in sight. *There, there,* I told myself, *people like us really are O.K.* Then the traitor Nicklaus abandoned me by losing all his fat, making himself lean and muscular, and going over to the ranks of the "normal."

And there are others, closer to home, who have recently robbed me of whatever unspoken comfort I have taken from miserable company. One of my dearest friends recently left me high and dry, transforming himself from a significantly overweight 220 to a trim 160. He has maintained his 160 for over a year now, and I have no hope that he will ever balloon back up to join me in flabby defiance of cultural ideals. If anything, he has taken it all to heart and honed his total appearance to accord with his new body. His new clothes, hairstyle, bearing, even his air of self-confidence—all reflect new appreciation of himself.

He is the one-in-twenty. I am surprised because he had been overweight all his life and seemed so accepting of the condition. On the other hand, he is a narrow-hipped man whose underlying physique never suggested it wanted the burden of extra bulk. And he is a phenomenally well-disciplined person whose concentration and determination were never in doubt. Once he dedicated himself to the task, there was simply no looking back.

But it makes me feel stupid.

If he can be the one in twenty, why can't I? Do I have to be one of the nineteen who maintain the odds? Other questions nag even more deeply: Is there some *reason* why all we other nineteen can't make it? Are we lacking something particular? Is there some magic ingredient? Could we, too, make it if only we had the——? The what? Willpower?

I could go berserk on the spot thinking that it's only a matter of "willpower." That is the cruelest lie fat people have to live with—the notion that their flab is public testimony to some deficiency in their own toughness. What a lot of crap! On top of all the other rotten feelings fat people have about themselves, telling them they could escape it all if only they had a little willpower is the ultimate insult.

I *hate* the thought that this is a matter of defective willpower, and I fiercely believe it is a lie. I think I know the difference between what kinds of behavior can be changed by turning on the willpower and what kinds can't. I have earned three academic degrees, and willpower counts in that kind of effort. I have started three businesses from scratch, and nobody does that without willpower.

I know that when I am losing on the tennis court because of my carelessness at strokes or lack of concentration and competitive fire, I can fix the problem with more willpower. And the first time I tried to run a half-marathon (thirteen-plus miles), the odds against me were ridiculous: I had never in my life run more than two miles, and an injury had kept me from running at all for the previous month. What's more, I weighed well over two hundred pounds. I had no right to believe I could complete the race. I knew that if I could, it would be on nothing but sheer willpower. Every step of the last eight miles was torture, but I found I could reach deeper and deeper and deeper than I ever dared, into reserves I never knew were there. It hurt more and felt better than anything I had ever done. It was a triumphant experience for me, one of the four or five most important accomplishments of my life. That was a challenge willpower could meet.

Dieting isn't.

Dieting is the Vietnam War of personal trials. It is guerrilla warfare. I can't see or find the enemy, and all my high-tech weapons are laughably useless. The enemy is both biological and psychological, drawing me to the pantry as instinctively as an animal is drawn to a salt lick or to a drink of water. And each time I am drawn to overeat, something bad gets reinforced in me. It's like a message that repeats over and over, *You are too weak to resist. You are doomed. Don't fight it. You are fat and will be fat forever.* After all these years, that message is like a stain that penetrates clear through me and can never come out.

No thin person can ever understand that. Thin people cannot possibly imagine walking toward the pantry while saying, "Don't do this." I am sure they consider it lack of
willpower to stand in the pantry spreading peanut butter on
a cracker while saying, "Don't do this." Or to put it in their
mouth while saying, "Don't do this."

That is clear evidence of lack of willpower, right?

Wrong.

It doesn't show lack of willpower. Here is what it shows:
*whatever it is that impels a fat person to eat is stronger than normal
willpower.* The word "normal" is critical. Unless slim people
conclude that all fat people reveal, by their very fatness, defective willpower, it just might be possible to offer us the
benefit of the doubt. Maybe—just once—they could concede
that some of us might, in fact, have as much willpower as
slim people do—perhaps even more, in some cases. Give us
a break. Willpower we've got; we've also got a problem slim
people don't have, which willpower just doesn't work on.

It would be nice if the slim world would get off our backs
about this, but I won't hold my breath. This one's going to be
with us for a long, long time, and I can tell by the strong feelings I get sitting here that this is not the last time I will want
to tackle the subject of willpower.

August 20. Weight: 205

I guess I'm starting to eat differently today—that is, to *diet*. I
know I said this experiment isn't about dieting, and it isn't.
But whatever problem I am grappling with requires a change
in eating, for sure, and I might as well introduce that factor
into the experiment as early as possible, to let it play its role.
I can't imagine how I could ever get a trimmer body without
a change in diet, so I'd better put that into the mix.

If people detect something less than outright enthusiasm on

my part, they are right. I have waddled down this road before. I don't like it. I expect annoyance on a day-to-day basis
and failure at the end.

Besides, I don't know why I should even try.

For a person who is embarking on something that's presumably self-improvement, I sure don't feel very enthusiastic
about it. Maybe this isn't the right time to start. Maybe I need
more of a kickoff, to catch myself at a peak of motivation.

No, timing has nothing to do with it.

I guess I always used to think it did. I thought if I could find
some milestone date, like New Year's Day or a major birthday or whatever, then I'd really get the urge to launch The
Diet To End All Diets. That would mark the changing of eras
for me, when I would quit the ranks of the overweight and
go over to the other side once and for all.

I am suddenly recognizing something—the part of the last
sentence, "go over to the other side," reveals something to
me I had never known before. If I change myself, I am going
to abandon a precious part of me, part of my inner self, part
of my personal history. Not pounds of flesh. Whole parts of
my very being.

That must be it. Being overweight has been so central a part
of me for my whole life up to now that I cannot just let go of
it like a worn-out pair of socks. Maybe what I am facing is the
most titanic struggle that has ever been put to me—nothing
less than letting go of a major dimension of my identity,
changing the very way I think of myself, the way I recognize
who I am.

God, I don't know whether I can do that.

How can being overweight be so important to me? How can

something I despise so much be so valuable? Maybe I'd better search through my memories to find how and why I am so attached to myself that way.

Here's what occurs to me first: I have made an enormous investment over my whole life up to now in inventing ridiculous reasons why it is O.K.—even *good*—to be fat. One incident epitomizes them all. I was nineteen years old.

I can remember the setting. Parked on Ocean Avenue in Carmel, California. Sitting in a black-and-white '55 Chevy two-door owned by my best friend in high school and college. (He, by the way, tipped the scales at a tidy 145 compared to my flabby 195.) I can't remember the conversation that led up to what I said, but I can remember what I said: "I'll bet the best way to build up a terrific physique is to be overweight. Carrying around an extra fifty pounds must be just like constant weight lifting. So once it has built you up, all you have to do is strip it off and—bingo!—underneath you have this great body."

For all I know, it *is* a wonderful theory. All except the part about stripping the fifty off.

That's what I am facing now. Making good on that part of the theory. Stripping it off, finding out what is underneath.

I just never realized I am going to have to go so *far* underneath to find out. Way past the forty pounds of fat. Way past simply changing the shape of my body. Way past making alterations in some of my clothes and replacing others.

I have to let a precious part of me die.

Damn it.

I don't know if I *can*. I fought so hard, so often, so painfully to defend the overweight me. Every day of my life. Every time I felt judged for my shape. Every time I couldn't do chin-ups in gym or climb the dumb rope to the rafters. Every time I skipped the shower after gym. Every time I looked in the mirror. Every time I approached a rack of slacks and discovered the sizes stopped short of my waist size. Every time I failed to approach a girl because I was sure she would slay me on the spot with the words, "Who'd want to go out with a fat guy like you? Yuk!" Every time someone made a smart crack about my flab.

Each incident has left its mark and made its contribution. As an oyster spins a pearl around the grating grain of sand in its gut, I spun some little tale of reassurance to myself around each painful incident. *You are O.K., Eliot. Really, you are,* I insisted. I worked so hard, so desperately to convince myself nothing was wrong. This is the way I am and it is all right. It is all right. It's all right.

Except it wasn't.

■ ■ ■

Why *isn't* it O.K. to be overweight?

Even the word *overweight* reeks of negative judgment. "Over" *what* weight?! I am not over *my* weight. What makes anybody think we all have to conform to some standard? Sure, I know all the life-insurance actuarial tables and "ideal" weights that are supposed to correlate with life span and all that. But so what?

I am not impressed with the health problem of being overweight. I really am not. That, despite the fact that I try to keep myself reasonably healthy and am fairly athletic. I work out at a gym three times a week, play tennis once or twice a week, and run a few miles several times a week as well. I am not impressed with the health risks, even though my business in health care keeps me in constant contact with the latest findings and leading thinkers.

I would never lose this extra forty for health reasons alone.

But that is the reason I would probably give someone if they asked me. Why? Because I hate to admit the real reason.

Social pressure.

Social pressure? What the hell kind of a reason is that for someone who is forty-seven years old and has successfully resisted that social pressure for nearly half a century? Why now all of a sudden?

I don't know. It just popped out. Perhaps I'll stumble onto the reason as I write.

Maybe it's the Chinese water-torture thing. The cumulative weight of all those years defending myself, all the excuses, and all the denial have finally worn me down.

Maybe it's because I'm edging up on fifty and have to make up my mind about the rest of my life, about how similar or how different it will be compared to what came before.

Or maybe I just can't stand the judgment against me anymore. I am sick and tired of being considered defective. I am sick and tired of being treated as an inferior by a jackass like Dick when I know he couldn't carry my jock in most areas of life.

I know that people who have never been overweight simply cannot—*cannot*—imagine what pain there is for overweight people as they catch a glimpse of themselves in others' eyes.

Painful as Dick's comment was, the cruelest thing anyone ever said to me was spoken by someone who is supposedly a friend. (I welcome friends who will say hard, challenging things to me; this was different.)

The setting couldn't have been more idyllic. We were together at an afternoon party on the deck of a summer cottage on the coast of Maine. Our hostess had baked some kind of confection that may well be the most memorable dessert I have ever put in my mouth. A light, meringuelike cake ribboned with undertones of vanilla and butterscotch and delicate caramel, it was nothing short of heaven. Each forkful melted in a gentle burst of fabulous sweetness. I have never enjoyed anything I have eaten more than I enjoyed that.

And so I turned to my friend, natty and flat-bellied in his nautical attire, and said he really must try some. He said nope so abruptly and forcefully I was prompted to ask why.

I wish I hadn't.

His answer: "Because I don't want to look like you."

■ ■ ■

What gives somebody the right to say something like that? Why would anybody stab another person with such a bitterly poisoned dagger? What could account for such a lack of civility, of sensitivity, of common decency? Yet it is a commonplace experience for fat people. We don't usually get bashed with such harsh words. But the judgment is still there, in other people's eyes. Fat people are yet another minority that society is prejudiced against—and perhaps the only one it's still socially permissible to ridicule and call hurtful names.

I have tried to justify my (ostensible) friend's horrifying insult, to excuse him somehow. I normally try to understand how and why other people behave as they do and to make allowances. But I have no feeling of goodwill toward those who reflect the trim-body ideal in their dealings with me. I experience them as judges—people who size me up and find me inadequate.

That makes me angry as hell.

And it makes me even angrier when they size me up and find me *adequate*. Anyone who has ever lost a chunk of weight knows what happens. Well-meaning people come up and ask an utterly predictable question and then pronounce an utterly infuriating judgment.

"Hey, haven't you lost some weight?"

"Yes."

"Well, you look terrific."

They probably expect me to feel flattered and say gratefully, "Oh, thank you so much." But, instead, I want to retort, "Go to hell, you goddamned jerk. By whose standard do I now look 'terrific'? Who says I looked less than terrific before? And who gives you the authority to pronounce such judgments? Shut up and get lost."

It is all I can do to stifle my violent urge to tell them off.

Of course, these people who think they are paying me a compliment can never understand the two reasons I hate their words. First, I *know*, deep in my heart of hearts, that I am going to regain the weight some day. I *know* the day will come when they will look at me once again and say (silently, I hope), "Looks like Eliot has put it all back on. Too bad he doesn't have any willpower." To me, their supposed praise is nothing but a curse with a delayed fuse.

But there is a second, more subtle reason I reject their words. *My true loyalty is not to this temporarily slimmed-down Eliot, but to the fat Eliot I have lived with and protected my whole life.*

I am not at all sure I can be faithful to him and still become a trimmer me. Forget the question of whether I can lose weight and keep it off—I honestly do not know if I *want* to, if it means cutting me off from my own history.

The fat Eliot goes back a long way and *is* me. We are insep-
arable. It is a struggle for me to recall how deeply my childhood revolved around eating, but when I do recall, I am
shocked and saddened at how completely my fatness has
shaped my life.

Maybe I was born fat. I know I was born heavy (almost ten
pounds), and so maybe I was also "born fat." I have a picture of my slender older brother at age four, with me beside
him at age two—plump, chubby. So whether I was born fat,
or seemingly born to be fat, is an open question I'll never
answer.

It didn't take me long to figure out that fat was a target. With
the innocent cruelty only children can inflict, my name Eliot
became "Elephant." I was doomed. I may have had some admirable qualities as a six- or seven-year-old, but they were
ignored by these classmates whom I also wanted to be my
playmates. What they saw was my fat. Kids have a way of
creating in-groups and outcasts, and fat Eliot was quickly
cast out.

Even at that tender age, I reacted in the self-defeating way
that people like me do: I isolated myself. I guess this is the
natural reaction of a creature that feels ashamed—you slink
off and hide somewhere. You curl up and lick your wounds.
Or an ice-cream cone. That's what I did. I hid out and ate,
and the more I ate the fatter I got. And, of course, the fatter
I got, the less chance there would ever be that the other kids
would let me be part of the in-group.

From the start, I scrounged money to spend on eating and I
spent it all. I mean *all*. My allowance went for Cheetos and
Necco wafers from the little grocery on my way home from
school. (Why Cheetos and Necco wafers? Despite the relative blandness of their taste, they had the overriding advantage of taking longer to eat than anything else.)

The nickel my mother gave for the collection plate as she sent me off to Mass on Sunday mornings went for a Hershey's bar at the bus station. It bothered me more than a little, to be sure, that I was stealing the nickel from *God*. In fact, as I bought my weekly Hershey's bar at the bus station with God's nickel, my recurring fantasy was that being an adult would mean having an endless supply of my very own guilt-free nickels to buy an endless supply of Hershey's bars.

Little did I suspect that the guilt over spending my own grown-up nickels in such a sneaky and self-destructive way would prove to be worse than the guilt I felt over "swiping them from God."

By the time I was eight, I had a paper route that gave me enough money to go on a real eating binge, where I could stuff myself with sweets until I was literally drunk with sugar.

I know that what I am going to write next sounds sick, but it was sick.

About my paper route. We lived in the steep California hills above Oakland and Berkeley, and during the years of World War II, various tradespeople sold meats or vegetables or dairy goods or housewares from trucks that combed the area. Since most women were at home in those days, cars were scarce, and gasoline was rationed by the gallon, these vendors, when they paused at intersections, found plenty of customers waiting.

The bakery truck also found a roly-poly eight-year-old newsboy who could be counted on to buy a dozen glazed donuts every day. Every single day. A dozen glazed donuts every single day. He ate them all himself. All by himself.

I can hardly believe it, as I recall it now. But I know, sadly, that it is true. Every day, I would rendezvous with the bakery truck at the same time, get my bag of donuts, promise the driver payment at the end of the month, and set out to deliver my sixty-six papers. I calculated to finish the last donut well before I arrived home, so no trace of my eating binge would be evident. Even then, I must have known there was something very wrong.

Something else was wrong, too, but it didn't seem to bother me at the time: when I collected the money from my subscribers at the end of each month, the portion I earned all went to the bakery man. All of it.

From the time he was eight until he was ten, the fat little newsboy scrambled two to three miles up and down steep hillsides lugging a heavy canvas sack of papers in all kinds of weather—just to binge on a dozen glazed donuts. I could weep for that lonely little boy today.

But the dull pain of that daily ritual didn't hurt as much as the humiliation I felt in just one day when I was eight. I was in the little corner grocery on my accustomed homeward stop for Cheetos or Necco wafers. That particular day it was Cheetos—a big box, family size. Just as I was making my purchase, I glanced up to see a car pulling into a parking spot in front—my father! What was *he* doing there at that time of the afternoon!? I didn't wait to find out. I bolted from the side door and crashed through the stacks of empty cardboard cartons behind the store in a blind frenzy, clutching my beloved Cheetos. Safe! I was sure Dad hadn't seen me. Rattled but relieved, I made my way home through the creek beds and woods, just to be sure we wouldn't meet up again before I had taken care of the Cheetos.

At home that evening, Dad took me aside and handed me a small amount of change. "The lady at Murphy's market said you left this behind in your hurry to get out of the store, El." He continued with a quiet, rather sad note: "I suppose it's all right to buy something extra to eat on the way home, but it does seem a little silly to be careless with the change."

That was the closest we came to having a conversation about my weight and my eating until seven years later when I was fifteen. It was also one of the most upsetting moments of my life. An eight-year-old boy does not want to be regarded as stupid by his father; after that, I wondered for a long time if he had any regard for me at all.

I don't know how or why my parents chose to ignore my problem—they were not unaware of my bulk. With her fondness for arcane words, my mother used to refer to it as my *avoirdupois*, an ancient term for heaviness. Dad called it my "beef." Looking back, I am mystified at their failure to provide me with any guidance or support. Perhaps it is just my selective memory, recalling what I want and forgetting what I'd rather not think about, but if they showed any concern during my childhood years, I cannot remember it now.

"El," Dad would say when faced with heavy lifting, "I need your beef over here." Since we were building a house together during my fourteenth and fifteenth years, I heard that fairly often.

And then once too often.

At the dinner table one night, Dad said something about my "beef" and I blew. I flew into an uncontrolled rage, screaming and crying and pleading for help.

"You think I like having fat jiggle all over my body! You think I *like* being valued more for my bulk than my brains! I can't *stand* it! I need your help, not your jokes!"

What I remember most was their surprise. I was astonished at their surprise. Even through my intense, searing rage at that moment, I realized what it meant: they didn't have a clue about the deep pain I had been suffering all those years. They knew I was fat all right, but they sure didn't know what it was like for me to be fat.

I know now that I have been alone in my fatness for my whole life, isolated inside a soft prison where I had only one friend I could count on. Myself. No wonder I find it so difficult—no, unthinkable—to consider abandoning that self with whom I have suffered through so much. Jack Nicklaus may have turned traitor on me, and my formerly fat friend too. But I'm not sure I can give up the bond between me and the fat person I have always been.

August 22. Weight: 204½

The change in eating (that is, diet) that I am sort of undertaking begins with a "cleansing" day or two. That's where I am now, cleansing myself. Day Two of self-cleansing. Not very inspiring, I can tell you. Neither the food—mostly exotic vegetable-based broths—nor the concept.

If I need cleansing, what made me dirty?

Well, actually, I must concede from previous experience that I really can tell the difference when I clear my system of certain foods. For example, I know that sugar is poison for me. The two times I lost thirty or so pounds, I was very aware that the total absence of sugar in my diet was making a major change in my body and in my urge to eat. That was when I knew for certain that the chemistry of my body—not willpower—was the key to weight control.

For me, the flip side of sugar is alcohol. When I drink alcohol, I am soon gripped by a craving for sugar. Any evening that includes drinking inevitably ends with my raiding the pantry or refrigerator for *anything* sweet—ice cream, cookies, candy, even peanut butter (most brands of which are apparently full of sugar).

The effects of those two substances are really dramatic. Once I have had any significant quantity of alcohol, I would "walk through a brick wall" to get something full of sugar. (I do not drink to excess and have felt inebriated only a couple of times since college.) I wish I understood more about the chemistry of all this, because I am truly helpless when whipsawed between alcohol and sugar. They trigger a reaction that demands more and more and more—of both of them.

So, if I'm going to change my ways (and shape) forever, I may have to consider permanently excluding some things from my diet that I'd rather not give up.

Well, if I have to change my ways, I guess I'll start with something I know can help me. I went on a vegetarian diet a few years ago that worked wonders. It was one I felt I could stay on forever if I had the time to do the daily shopping and prepare the fairly sophisticated recipes. Well, that's what I have returned to today, just to get started. And it will eliminate sugar from my diet for a while—until I feel free of its influence, or until I concede I'm fat forever.

I am not crazy about the idea of going a lifetime without some of the things I love so much, but I have to begin somewhere. So I am starting with vegetarian stuff. I am somewhat less than thrilled at the prospect.

August 25. Weight: 206

Today didn't start too well.

For the past four days, I have been laid out flat in bed, owing to severe lower back pain. This has kept me away from my typewriter and has diluted my interest in the experiment. Pain has a way of diverting the mind and sapping all energy. My week has passed in a vague blur of VCR movies and visits to a doctor who brings me gradual relief from the damnable stabs of pain.

The last thing on my mind has been the question of my shape.

But by this morning, the pain had receded enough to let me think about resuming the experiment—and my writing about it. I figure to be good for about two or three half-hour stints at the typewriter today, separated by hour-long rests flat on my back. Which is fine for the mechanics of writing; but what about the experiment?

I came downstairs to face the question of whether I wanted to eat sensibly today—that is, to reduce weight—or whether to glide along. My weight is up a few pounds (to 206) as the result of casual eating and inactivity this week. Why not just let it ride there until some good impulse or motivation comes along to get me started losing weight again?

I shuffled toward the kitchen, taking care as I do these days to take baby steps that won't awaken new twinges of pain. I began to focus mildly on the question of whether I would structure my eating today or graze mindlessly. Surveying the scene only made my indecision more troublesome; there was plenty of stuff for sensible eating—fruit, bran, skim milk—and lots of the good stuff too—English muffins, butter, jams, eggs, and cheeses.

My wife settled the question for me.

As I awoke, she was just leaving the house and said something to me that I dimly began to recall, almost an hour after arising: "Your breakfast is out on the porch."

This morning, the glass-topped table held a neatly laid tray with a sensible breakfast: grapefruit juice; homemade cereal of dry bran, wheat germ, sunflower seeds, and raisins; a pitcher of skim milk; a thermos of fresh coffee; and two slices of sweet cantaloupe.

It was just what I needed. No, no, not nutritionally—although I needed it for that too. It was what I needed to keep me from making a decision I would have regretted.

I am puzzled by my reaction. Ordinarily, there is almost nothing I resent more than my wife's playing *any* role whatsoever in my weight management. I have long since detected and reacted badly to even the most subtle strategies she has adopted to help me with this problem. I appreciate her concern and I understand why she wants to help, but as anyone who fights this fight knows, it is a misguided effort.

I am sure she worries about my weight. She knows that my family health history includes some bad hearts and terrible blood pressure, along with diabetes. My own blood pressure has been right at the borderline of requiring medication for twenty years now and recently has slipped into the danger zone. I expect to be on medication shortly.

And, although she has never said anything and never would, it is hard to imagine she doesn't think I would *look* better if I weighed less. Let's face it, spouses do care about the appearance of their mates, and I am not exactly a matinee idol.

Trish really does care for me, and she has no doubt I would feel better about myself without all this extra weight. But she has also experienced my sometimes passive and sometimes explosive resistance to any effort on her part to help me. I have resented it and have displayed that resentment in a hundred ways.

My resentment is probably more poisonous than it might otherwise be because, after being my overeating buddy for a while, she has mastered the problem herself.

I met my wife-to-be at a casual party, we talked nonstop for eight days, decided to marry each other, and did. In the three months between that eighth day and our wedding, I lost thirty or forty pounds and was, on our wedding day, truly trim for the first time in my life.

It was to be the last time in almost thirty years. By our six-month anniversary I had gained it all back, a feat made easier by our decision to move to a small Danish community in California dominated by Danish bakeries. We binged our way through many a display case of pastries in those first six months—and for the rest of the time we lived there too. We developed some habits that rivaled my daily dozen donuts as a paperboy. One of the local bakeries, just a merciful block and a half from our apartment, turned out fresh pecan pies on Saturday morning. I was there when it opened, and my wife and I polished off an entire pecan pie topped with whipped cream for *breakfast* every Saturday for almost two years.

With twenty other meals a week to account for, and plenty of snacks in-between, the shopkeepers were kept busy supplying us with shortbread, sticky buns, and other delights besides the normal pastries and breads. Whatever anxieties we experienced as newlyweds and rookie teachers, we found no difficulty in burying them under an avalanche of extraordinary baked goods.

But even though we both gained a goodly amount of weight during those two years, only I kept mine on. Trish rather quietly altered her eating pattern, undeterred by my continued overeating. Her determination to take care of herself gained impetus when she became pregnant at the end of our second year of marriage. From then on, she kept herself in good shape.

I probably resent that more than I care to admit. I thought Trish would be a reliable co-conspirator for a lifetime of overeating, but she had other ideas. I wish I could get myself off the hook by saying she had it easier—wasn't fat as a child, was stimulated to manage her weight when she got pregnant, and so on. But it doesn't work. I think I have to live with the fact that she handled this thing better than I did.

That's why I don't know why her effort to guide my eating this morning felt so good. It wasn't like her to do it, and it isn't like me to like it.

Maybe I know, at long last, that I need help.

August 30. Weight: 206½

The voice came from behind me, over my shoulder. The tone was gentle and insistent, confidential, earnest. "Do you mind if we talk about something you haven't asked me about?"

Given my position at the time, my options were limited. I was spread-eagled, face down, on a doctor's treatment table, and the man behind the voice was applying ultrasound to my damaged lower back muscles, the ones that have kept me laid out and hobbling for almost two weeks now. It was my sixth visit to him in nine days, and we are beginning to feel like friends.

I guessed he was going to discuss resumption of sexual activity after my treatment regimen, which has excluded almost all physical movement. Nothing I'd rather talk about.

"Of course not," I said into my folded arms. "What's on your mind?"

"How do you feel about your weight?"

Oh, swell. Just what I needed.

That was yesterday. Today I realize it *was* just what I needed. It has been about four or five days since I wrote anything. For most of that time I have been enjoying lazy days at home—lazy because my doctor ordered me to do next to nothing; lazy because it is late August and doing next to nothing comes very naturally; lazy because my daughters Anne (twenty-one) and Patricia (nineteen) have been busily packing for their return to college, and they are at the stage where they'd really rather do it themselves, thank you.

So I chat with them a little, snack a little, read a little, snack a little, watch a movie on the VCR and snack a little, and snack a little more. I also eat three full meals, of course.

That's what I meant about my doctor's comment being just what I needed; his timing coincided perfectly with my own body's telling me it is time to *do* something.

I really do feel that need strongly now. After years of regular and strenuous physical activity, problems with my knees and my lower back have kept me all but sedentary for four or five months—and practically bedridden for two weeks. My body is screaming for exercise.

And after no prompting from anyone but myself for quite a while now, someone who cares about me professionally is asking me why I am fat.

So today is a day I can take seriously, as Day One of getting slim. The kids left for school this morning. Physically I am up and around now. I'll be back at the office in about five days and won't be near the kitchen except at breakfast and dinner hours. That'll help, not being able to cruise through there out of sheer boredom.

And finally, this is as good a day as any to be the first day of the rest of my life. I am beginning a major new business venture next Tuesday. My wife is beginning a major new step in her professional career the following week. Our son, Alan, sixteen, is transferring to a new school that same week.

So all the pieces are in place. Now, I just have to fit myself into a picture that includes them all—and a slim me.

I don't know who I am slim. I don't know what I look like, let alone how to think about the me that looks like that. The unanswered question of what I would look like, of who I would be, looms like a barrier. But maybe one way to get over that barrier would be to see what I would look like without fat. For instance, I wonder what it would be like to have a picture of myself forty pounds lighter. If I had that picture and looked at it every day, lived with it, imagined myself into it, what would happen? Could I get comfortable with it? Come to want what I see? Reject it?

I remember when I was a teenager, I had a patchwork vision of myself with a great body. I used to look in envy at the muscular, athletic bodies of some of my high school class-mates and think to myself, *Now if I just had his body and my head.* . . . And I could *almost* see what the result would be.

But that was thirty years ago. Now I have gray hair, a double chin, a bad back, and signs of aging that deny such simple-minded fantasies. I need a new vision, one of the me I know and really love. The me that is packed with forty-seven years of wonderful experiences and relationships and disappoint-ments and achievements. I want to see how *that* me would look in a body free of flab. I wonder if I could really get that kind of a picture of me somehow. Sure, there must be a way.

By God, I'll do it.

II

I am really desperate.

September 9. Weight: 203

The last few days have been a roller coaster, some days eating like a man who really believed in getting slim and healthy—and other days stuffing myself until I was uncomfortable. What I have finally come to realize is that I need a—I hate to even write the word—a *diet*. God, I loathe the word *diet!* All it has ever meant to me is deprivation of pleasure followed by defeat of intent.

And yet, the truth is, if I just continue to graze my way through the kitchen and the stores, I'm not going to get anywhere at all in this experiment. All the writing and thinking in the world won't change me if I don't change the kind and amount of food I put down the hatch each day.

So I have resumed a food plan (see, I can't even repeat the "d" word!) that had been very successful for me a number of years ago. Based on the cuisine of a spa called The Golden Door, the plan requires a lot of time for shopping and preparing meals, but it *does* work. The meals taste good, fill me up, and are undeniably healthy.

So figure this out: after dinner, while alone in the house and not in the least bit hungry, I ate two large crackers (the two-by-four-inch size) plain; two more spread with peanut butter; a small dish of grape-nuts; two handsful of peanuts; a slice of honeydew melon.

The horrible part is this: before each raid—I am talking about six different trips from wherever I was to the kitchen—I had a debate about whether I would sabotage the new diet. My head said no. My body said yes. Actually, that's not true. It wasn't my body. I asked my body if it was hungry and it wasn't. I was *not* hungry. Whatever in me wanted—six times—to put something down the hatch was neither my head nor my body.

It was my enemy.

What kind of enemy is this, anyhow? What kind of power can turn me into a whimpering baby, can turn every power of intellect and will into useless mush, can brush aside almost fifty years of development as a person? Is this a *disease?* What other word fits for something that so effectively invades my body and my mind, luring me toward . . . toward death.

That *is* what it is—a disease—and that *is* what it is doing— killing me. Can there be any doubt?

God help me.

September 12. Weight: 201½

This gets more complicated all the time. I mean, the more I think about myself and eating, about the interplay between my life and food, the more I discover the centrality of the issue.

Case in point: the remodelling of our house. We live in a turn-of-the-century house with too many interior walls for my taste. We moved here from a wide-open, contemporary house where one room flowed into every other. We were constantly in sight of each other. In this old house we recently moved to, we felt cut off from each other.

So we started knocking down walls, beginning with the kitchen. What we wound up with was not so much a kitchen with a sitting area as a den you could cook in. Now it is what it should be—the heart of the house. We all gravitate to it naturally, to warm ourselves by the fireplace and by each other's company. And to feed ourselves with the food that's always within reach. Eating together is really a way of communing with each other.

And that goes beyond family; we have a unique, food-based relationship with two sets of friends who live across the street. (They are the reason we bought this house, so we could live in a cluster.) We cook for each other. Every Tuesday, we cook a triple-sized portion of whatever we're having for dinner, and then we deliver the two extra portions to their homes. Wednesdays and Thursdays they do the same. Often, we just gather at one house to eat as one big extended family.

So I am wondering: if I stick to some oddball diet, am I going to lose those precious ties in some way? Is this going to be grammar school all over again, with everybody else in the in-group, and me a one-man out-group? Damn.

September 13. Weight: 201½

I am feeling a little desperate this morning. The scale is stuck at 201½ and has been for a number of days now. I know from past experience with this diet that it shouldn't be. In fact, *any* diet that limited caloric intake to one thousand or twelve hundred calories a day should create a lot of downward movement in weight.

I must be cheating too much.

That's a funny concept, cheating. I suppose it is simply another way of describing the sabotaging I described earlier, of giving it a name. But it is a name that is somehow appropriate, because when applied to a diet, it tries to make playful the use of a word that is really quite nasty. *Cheating.* If there is one thing that makes almost anybody angry, it is a cheater. We all try to play fair, and a cheater becomes the target for the righteous wrath of everyone who has ever been tempted to take unfair advantage and decided against it.

But when a dieter uses the term playfully, it's as though we're saying, *Don't take me too seriously. I'm not really expecting too much of this diet—or myself.* It must be how we defend ourselves against the disappointment we know is just around the corner, when the weight comes right back on. The truth is, this is a love/hate experience. Part of me clearly wants to win, but the rest of me—how much? the majority?—wants me to fail. My cheating is the hub of it all.

I seem to cheat in two widely different situations—either when I am all alone, or when I am in a particularly convivial group. At a party or in a restaurant with family and other friends, I will almost always decide to "join in" the pattern of eating rather than stick to my diet. I'm sure I just don't want to be set apart anymore than I already feel set apart.

But when I am cheating all alone—that is the genuinely confusing part of it all. How many times have I stood in front of the refrigerator casing the contents, *looking* for something I knew I was not supposed to eat, *knowing* I was looking for something I was not supposed to eat, *telling* myself I was looking for something I was not supposed to eat, *telling* myself to stop looking for something I was not supposed to eat? And going ahead anyhow?

Which me am I cheating? Which me is the *real* me, anyhow?

I guess I had better face once again, more harshly this time, whether I am really serious about wanting to succeed.

Cheating. Cheating whom? Why? What rules are violated? Who set them? Do I acknowledge them? Who judges? What are the penalties? Does it all matter?

The sloppy answer to the question, Cheating whom? is cheating myself. But forget that. It's too easy. Let's get serious, Eliot. Cheating whom? I think it's closer to the truth to say it is cheating those who have voiced (silently or otherwise) the ideal, the standard that I have never measured up to. Maybe this is a way of giving them all the finger, refusing to conform to their criteria of acceptability. Sure, I'll make a show of struggling to comply, but I won't let myself succeed.

But probably "them" is only part of the answer to the question, Cheating whom? It must be much more complex than that. Some of the resistance to following a strict diet must lie in my own purely self-defeating instincts. I know we all hinder our own success in various ways, and I may be tripping myself up in this experiment. Why? Ah, now it begins to feel like we are getting somewhere—an answer bubbles up in my mind and it says, *Fear.*

Fear? Fear. Yes, I guess I do feel some fear of success in changing my body shape and all the personal habits that go along with it. I had better explore this fear.

The first thing that comes to mind is what fantasies I have about lean, taut people. I think of them as severe. Ascetic. Hard-nosed disciplinarians. Antipleasure. Excessively focussed on their bodies. Not too warm or approachable. Judging.

I also imagine that to be like them is to miss out on much of what I enjoy most in life. I am anything but severe and hard-nosed. I am rather agreeable and casual. I don't mind being agreeable and casual and it hasn't hurt me so far—except, perhaps, for the bulge around my middle. And I can drum up enough self-discipline to get my work done—and to write these pages at five in the morning.

The rest of my fantasies about lean people—that they are antipleasure, obsessed with a trivial subject, uncongenial, judging—add up to a picture of unfriendliness. They add up to people who set themselves apart from others by their devotion to their body and miss, in the process, so much of what makes human life human.

By now, of course, I realize how silly this sounds and how farfetched is the prospect that I would ever become so fanatical about it. Now that I think about it, an even more telling question stops me in my tracks: *Eliot, can you name one single example, in real life, of the kind of character you just described? Go ahead: name just one.*

I can't.

And since I can't, I have to face a painful conclusion: this must simply be more of the me-versus-them feelings leaching to the surface, the lifelong feelings of being out of it because of my body shape.

In other words, this must be pure jealousy. Pure and ugly.

The jealousy over not having a trim body, the resentment over being judged inadequate, the excuse-making and the sour grapes. Aw, who wants to be like them anyhow?

This hurts a lot. Really a lot. Do I have to go on with this? Can I begin to admit how much I do want to be like them? Do I dare to let loose the years and nights and endless moments of begging to be like them?

God, I feel it so deeply and so strongly in me, this aching to *look* like them but *act* like me.

Suddenly, I realize how completely the adolescent Eliot is still with me. I remember again when I was in high school, how I used to salve my bad feelings about myself and my body by fantasizing a composite me. Looking at a classmate with a fine physique, I would imagine what a great package it would make if I just had his body and my head. I always wanted to be me—in the head—and not someone else—but, oh, how deeply I yearned for me to be me atop a different body. Perhaps I should explore that some more. But not just now. Right now I need to give myself over to feeling, not thinking.

I feel a quiet sadness rising gently within me as I realize how long I have lived with this yearning—and the sour self-loathing that has accompanied it all these years. There is something genuinely sad, almost tragic in a small way, about getting this far in life without having dealt with this issue.

But better late than never. Dealing with it is, after all, what the experiment is about.

I just didn't expect it to uncover so much intimate unfinished business.

Now I feel like the subject of cheating is almost beside the point. I will undoubtedly come back to it one day before long, but for now I am more interested in exploring the subject of fear. If I can get behind the veil of fear in the days ahead, I may uncover stuff that explains cheating and other self-defeating behavior.

I hope I am equal to the challenge.

September 14. Weight: 201

I'm afraid it is time to rummage through some of my earlier pain, to find out where those wracking feelings of jealousy and yearning come from. They must go way back, probably to the years when peer groups and boy/girl relationships were being formed. Back to the days, that is, when I yearned to be accepted as an insider and was, instead, being confirmed as an outsider.

Back to junior high school.

Junior high school was where girls began to matter and where your worth as a young man was defined in relation to girls and to "the guys."

I hadn't needed to relate much to girls in grammar school. A few female classmates were friends, largely because we were equally good at our studies and found ourselves thrown together on projects, contests, and nonathletic extracurricular activities like plays and choirs. But nobody was dating in those days.

Junior high was different. All of a sudden, girls were no longer classmates; now they were objects of passionate, secret desire. They were both the cause of, and the answer to, the sexual urges that raced through me, thrilling and confusing and scaring me all at the same time. Girls took on godlike power in my life.

All of a sudden, appearance *really* mattered. The guys who were lean and limber and had some muscle definition moved smoothly and swiftly to the top of the social heap, winning the admiring glances of classmates of both sexes. Not even a face full of acne wrapped around a room-temperature IQ could block the ascendancy of a well-muscled stud who not only had a great physique but *knew* it. Now I was further out of it than I had ever been before. And I had less hope than before of ever getting in.

So while the real studs of our junior high were hanging out with the girls and learning anatomy firsthand, I spent my time fantasizing about one particularly well-developed girl and concentrating on my grades and citizenship. I must have done just fine at those second-choice pursuits, judging from the raft of awards I won at graduation.

I'd have traded them all for just one chance to slip a trembling hand over the warm softness that swelled Sandra's bra.

But that was not to be. I settled for swiping quarters from my mother's purse every afternoon and heading for a little six-stool mom-and-pop coffee shop on McKinley Street where a grilled cheese sandwich cost fifteen cents and a dish of ice cream a dime—my junior-high equivalent of the daily dozen donuts.

Junior high school also made worse—and more official—another insult I had almost managed to tolerate back in grammar school—choosing up sides for athletic games at recess on the playground. Knowing you'll be the last to be picked isn't a sweet thought. So back in grammar school days I would comfort myself by remembering that in the classroom I was usually the first to be picked in choosing up sides for a quiz or spelling bee. That helped a little, standing on the playground with my head hung down, listening to a pair of cocky jocks trade picks of my classmates until, with a shrug and a smart-ass comment, one was stuck, at the very last, with me.

"Come on, Fatso. Just try to keep out of the way, O.K.?"

But in junior high school, the classroom games at which I excelled disappeared, and along with them, any chance to get the approval I wanted from my classmates. My teachers may still have thought I was something special, but teachers can never make you feel O.K. the way your classmates can. Teachers' approvals can make you feel like a good student, but only your classmates can make you feel like a good *person*.

And so on the playground I had no place to turn to make myself feel O.K. Worse, we now had an official class called gym, and what had been an informal and occasional humiliation by classmates during grammar school recess now became a regular, daily, formal humiliation led by a skilled professional—the coach.

Coaches hate fat kids.

It's just that simple. Or at least the coaches that ran the gym classes at Hamilton Junior High in the late forties seemed to hate a fat kid named Eliot. I must have been a constant rebuke to their goals. Coaches always have goals—higher, faster, farther, and all that. I was lower, slower, and nearer. It drove them nuts. And as a result, they had no misgivings about permitting or perhaps even encouraging my classmates to mimic their practiced contempt for the way I cast dishonor on the glories of athletic achievement.

"O.K., class, everyone run four laps around the field, and the last one to finish goes through the mill."

I always knew who was doomed to be last—and be put "through the mill." It seems so barbaric, remembering it now. The rest of the class members line up, one behind the other, and form a tunnel between their legs. The guy going through the mill has to crawl on his hands and knees through their legs while they paddle his butt as he passes under them. The experience doesn't do much for your ego, and it hurts like hell to boot.

I suppose the fat kids represent everything coaches fear most, their own worst nightmare for what they themselves might have been—or might yet become. Whatever the case, the coaches in my life made gym exercises and contests a daily hell, surpassed only by the gang shower afterward.

Taking a shower with a couple of dozen other people has never been my idea of a good time. With one other person, yes. But a group, no. Especially a group who, for the last forty-five minutes, have watched their role model, the coach, show them new ways to castigate the fat kid who couldn't do any push-ups, couldn't go hand over hand even one inch up the damned rope climb, couldn't outrun a single person in the one hundred-yard dash. And now here he is, all blubbery too-much of him, shiny-wet and awkward, exposing the most inviting (and unmissable) target for towel-snapping.

Unfortunately, showers were mandatory.

It was during these years that I discovered the use of clothes to disguise my hated flab. I mostly wore the baggiest shirts I could find, and they obscured my shape somewhat. Too bad I didn't realize this strategy had its limits. Because, on the rare occasions when I was forced to go swimming in the company of females my age (something I was amazingly re-sourceful at avoiding, as you might imagine), I simply wore a tee shirt with my swimming trunks. Brilliant, no?

In recent years, I have seen the artful use of the wet tee shirt. Madison Avenue advertising people have recognized that it is truly a wonderful way to exaggerate the contours of the body—as in displaying the more appealing features of some astoundingly sexy young woman emerging from the water, beckoning us all to visit the Bahamas or some such place where, presumably, she or one of her friends awaits to favor us with sensual pleasures.

The sight of this thirteen-year-old's body with twenty-five or thirty extra pounds of soft fat jiggling under a wet tee shirt must have been a real turnoff for Sandra and her pals.

My high school experience was no great improvement over junior high. All kinds of people sized me up and remarked, "Say, you're a big kid. Ya goin' out for football?" I heard that often enough to give it a try. But I learned quickly enough that bulk is no substitute for ability, and after I got trampled a few times, I quickly retired from the game in favor of more after-school visits to the soda fountain.

Socially, it was more of the same. Sure that no self-respecting girl would want to date a fat guy, I hesitated to make any overtures. (I dated food instead.) And since much of the so-cial life in our hot-climate farming town centered around swimming, where my flabby body would be too exposed, I ducked invitations. I had at least learned by then that wet tee shirts were a poor disguise for a fat belly.

It seems kind of funny now. So why did I begin weeping as soon as I started writing about it this morning?

September 19. Weight: 201

I can't fool myself any longer: my actions show I am not giving this experiment my best. After two weeks of supposedly being on a diet—a diet on which I've lost weight in the past *and* eaten well—I am right where I started.

The time is perfect for losing weight. I'm under almost no stress. Work is going well. The kids are well settled and delighted with school. Trish and I have never had more fun together. And to top it off, she is temporarily at home to cook the marvelous dishes this diet calls for. Yes, all the conditions are right.

I guess I am not.

What the hell is wrong with me? Why can't I plunge into this once-in-a-lifetime (*last*-in-a-lifetime) chance and blast through to that new territory that . . . that *what?*

I can't write ". . . that I long for." Because I don't. I guess that is really important for me to understand. I do not long to be slim.

I want only to be O.K.

Yes, that's it. If being just the way I am were O.K., I'd be content. Though I am not thrilled with the way I look, I'd be satisfied. I am not terrified of the health problems that come with weighing a few extra pounds. And I get a lot of day-to-day pleasure from good food and drink and from all the companionship that goes with them.

Maybe the truth is that I do not have the amount of drive I need to change my life, habits, and pleasures to have a body that society will stamp USDA Prime. After all, even though I want and sometimes long to be considered O.K., it's hardly a wish that rules my life. If I were listing the things that are important to me, having a body that meets society's standards would have a hard time making it into the top ten—

despite my spending all this time and thought wrestling through the issue. This experiment just happens to pull together in one major lump a lifetime of minor—in fact, almost insignificant—feelings. (Oh, yeah? Well, not long ago that lump of minor feelings had a grown man remembering them in tears.)

I am plenty satisfied with who I am, with my family and friends, with the worthwhile work I do, and with my accomplishments. I can get along without the final satisfaction of society's approval of my body.

I wonder if I can get along without my own approval of it, though. Could I ever accept that I tried and failed to truly understand whatever it is that keeps me fat? Probably not.

I guess I'll just have to dig deeper and deeper into my store of energy to find something new to fuel the drive to understand this problem and overcome it. I can't quit, even though I don't fully know—yet—why I want to go on.

This all reminds me of a deadly serious conversation Trish and I had one afternoon on what felt like the last day of our marriage. Many years ago, we went through the usual struggles of young couples, dealing with job stresses, children, sharing housework, and our roles as husband or wife and parents, all of which are now comfortably settled.

We saw a counselor. After a number of unproductive sessions, our therapist finally put it on the line: "I really can't see any reason for you two to keep at this," she said. "You are having the same old arguments you've had for fifteen years, and you'll be having them for the rest of your lives. Perhaps it really is time for you to divorce."

Divorce. The word shocked me like a bucket of cold water. I shivered and tried to shake it off. But the counselor wouldn't let us sidestep it and insisted that we begin planning our divorce.

And so Trish and I drove into the countryside and sat in our convertible one sunny afternoon, overlooking a beautiful valley, and set about hacking our life and our love into ragged parts. A passerby would have mistaken us for lovers spinning dreams.

We got it all figured out. Who would live where. When we would see the children and each other. About the money and all that. The whole thing. Decent, civilized, friendly almost. Sad. No, tragic. But we worked it all through.

Then we chucked the plan and drove home. We simply refused to accept divorce as inevitable. Been together ever since. Thank God.

I feel the same do-it-anyhow feeling about getting rid of my fat. At the moment, I can't imagine any satisfactions that are worth the hassle of losing weight, any more than Trish and I could imagine any satisfactions in staying married when we decided to go home together that day. But something won't let me call it quits.

Let me add that there is no comparison between the two. My family is the heart and soul of my life; my body shape is petty by comparison. Besides, I truly knew how satisfying my family life could be because I had experienced it. That helped me stay married. I have never experienced being free of fat and cannot imagine what satisfactions it could possibly bring that would have real, deep meaning to me.

Again, I feel handicapped because I have no vision of the future Eliot to work toward that balances my history, my habits, my loyalty to the fat self that has always been me. I need to construct a clearer and sharper goal.

Maybe it is time to make good on my idea to get a portrait of myself the way I would look slimmed down. It seems hokey, but I have to start somewhere, I guess. I'm tired of spinning my wheels.

September 21. Weight: 198

Now this is more like it. Yesterday, 200¼; today, 198. I like it! No tiptoeing down to 199⁹⁄₁₀ as a way of crossing the barrier. Boom! Jumped right through it! I'm feeling some momentum now.

Don't ask me how long it will last, but I can feel it all around me—and in me. Yesterday, I was scrupulous about keeping to my diet and it really paid off. Of course, what kept me scrupulous was knowing that the payoff would be breaking the two hundred barrier. I also know how disappointed I would be if I didn't and how, by contrast, that would trip up my momentum. By the time I went to bed, I was so confident that I had made it that I wanted to weigh myself right then. But I didn't dare, because I knew there was a chance the effects of the day wouldn't show, and I didn't want to sleep on disappointment.

I haven't stopped to figure out why, all of a sudden, I'm talking as though I believe in this effort. I still don't know that I will see it through successfully—or that I want to. But for the moment, I know at least that the effort is bringing me back to where I have been for most of my life, around 195, and that is exciting in itself. Among other benefits, it will mean that a couple of suits I haven't been able to wear since I bought them while dieting a year ago will probably fit me again soon, just in time for fall.

The question is still open, though, about how it will feel going into foreign territory south of 195. But I am going to get some help. I am going to get that portrait of how I would look at 160 pounds.

No, no, I really mean it this time. I've *done* it. This isn't another of those, *Yes, by golly, I sure will do that one of these days.* I got sick of hearing that unkept promise. So yesterday I called the local art association.

"You want someone who can do *what?*" the politely perplexed voice at the association asked.

"Draw a full-length portrait of me the way I look now, probably in a swimsuit, and then draw another portrait of me the way I would look if I weighed forty pounds less."

"Wellll," she drew out, probably stalling for time while she figured out whether I was a genuine kook or just a part-time one, "I'm going to have to let you talk to somebody else who might know about that kind of thing. It's not, er, our usual. . . ."

"I understand," I went on, "but if you could just give me the names of a couple of artists who are experienced in drawing figures and doing portraits, I'm sure we can work it out. I work professionally with other kinds of artists all the time." I went on to describe my business and took pains to convey my sanity and sincerity.

"I may know someone who can help you out. One of our instructors here at the art association specializes in portraits. Pat Hamm's the name." She gave me a phone number. "Pat's really good," she added. "Just finished a fabulous portrait of Brooke Shields."

Swell. Just what I need—a chance to traumatize a first-rate artist by asking her to go from an artistic masterpiece, which celebrates a most admired face and figure, to a dismal display of my bulges, ripples, and extra folds of flesh. I don't care who Pat Hamm is—you can't go from sessions with beautiful Brooke Shields to sessions with flabby Eliot without suffering some trauma.

I dialed the number anyhow.

Pat turned out to be a woman, and she was definitely a little wary at the outset. Her initial lack of warmth tempted me momentarily to shrink back from my determination to follow through. *After all,* I told myself, *do you really want the humiliation of posing in a studio while the eyes of a sophisticated artist survey every misshapen bulge on your pudgy body? You have trouble enough with the nitwits who spontaneously size you up and find your body offensive; why pay good money to a stranger to repeat the insult?*

I persisted anyhow. "You see," I said to Pat, "this is a kind of experiment. I am trying to settle once and for all whether I will remain fat or become something approaching slim. But I have this hunch that one thing that keeps fat people from changing is that they don't know—can't envision—what they are changing *into*. A version of me without fat is a stranger to me, and I want to see that version so I can make friends with it—with me, that is, wearing a different body."

I braced myself for a snicker from her or a click from the receiver. What I heard instead was music: "I just lost forty pounds myself this past year, and I think your hunch is fascinating. I'd love to do it."

We quickly settled on a fee and a date. I am to show up at her studio next Tuesday at 1:00 P.M.

September 23. Weight: 199½

I let my guard down yesterday and—whap!—I really got smacked. The day started out fine. I had lost yet another pound and weighed in at 197½. Nice way to start a beautiful fall Saturday. I felt no particular need to write, so I gave myself the day off from that. I ate a cautious breakfast—strictly by the book. Same routine at lunch.

Trouble began when Bert called. Since our wives were away for the weekend at an antiques auction, how about dinner at his house? I should have known that going to his house meant that he had set the menu. Maybe I really wanted what was to come.

What came first from the oven was a huge roasting pan heaped with Doritos laced with cheese sauce. He surrounded it with big bowls of guacamole, refried beans, sour cream with chopped scallions. And more: chopped tomatoes and plump olives were set out. And cold Dos Equis beer, of course. My favorite.

Well, I told myself, *things have gone well. You can have just a bit of all this as a reward. Or, come to think of it, just dig in and consider this your dinner* (knowing full well that more was to come). What else came? Charcoal-broiled steaks, baked potatoes with butter and sour cream, green salad with blue cheese dressing. A nice wine too.

All of which appeared on my body this morning as two extra pounds of fat. That is a major one day gain.

Worse, I knew I was looking into the face of defeat. Is this the beginning of the end, or just a slip I can recover from? Have I ruined the good chemistry that has made it so easy to diet and lose weight the last few days? I don't know the answer to these questions, but I'd better find out fast because the next big test is just hours away.

My partner and I are hosting a party at our office to celebrate five years of successful collaboration. A few dozen friends and business associates will gather around some fancy foods and expensive wines. This is going to be a test for me. As soon as I get back, I'll sit down here again and record how it went.

September 23—Continued

The party was supposed to last for two hours. And for two hours my discipline held up fine. I nursed a glass or two of Perrier and ignored the platters of delicacies.

The party went on another hour but my discipline didn't. In that final hour, I got into the champagne, cheese, nuts, and a few other goodies. If I could have quit then, everything might have been, well, if not great, at least tolerable. But, of course, some friends suggested dinner together and guess where I wound up? Back at Bert's house. Same overload of food on the table. Same overload in my belly. No, worse. Big dessert tonight as well.

Tomorrow morning I will weigh 201½ or so, having destroyed my big breakthrough of the 200 barrier. I am discouraged and depressed. I did not do anything different tonight than anyone else did—in fact, I was significantly more disciplined than almost anyone else in the place, but tomorrow morning I will be ruined. It doesn't seem fair, does it?

September 24. Weight: 201¼

I am so damned discouraged I feel like junking this whole mess. As predicted, I am boldly above the two hundred barrier again, a barrier more easily penetrated going north than south. I feel angry and frustrated and cheated.

I feel cheated that I cannot go to a couple of parties and not come home *hugely* fatter. How come other people can spend those few hours the very same way I did, eating and drinking the same things I did, and not bulge out and bulk up as a result?

Look, it's only about forty-eight hours since I woke up weighing 197½. I was perfectly disciplined except for three times—a total of about six or seven hours—and yet I gained *four* pounds? What the hell is going on here, anyhow! Four goddamned pounds? Impossible! They say it takes thirty-five hundred extra calories to make an extra pound. Come on, I didn't take in fourteen thousand *extra* calories in those few hours.

That's why I feel cheated. If I didn't take on that caloric load, why did I take on those extra pounds?

At this point, I would gladly trash this whole experiment. If all it were designed to do was help me get skinny, I'd be off it this instant. But it isn't. It is to help me *understand* what's going on here. That is all that keeps me going this morning. It sure isn't the prospect of being tied for the rest of my life to a body chemistry that punishes me so severely every time I relax my grip the least bit. I don't want any part of that. I'll do it for purposes of understanding, but not as a permanent way of life.

I suppose this is a dead-end street, grumping about how unfair it is that I get fat while others don't. I doubt it will lead to much understanding, anyhow. I would do better to look at my behavior last night and figure out why I was unable to abstain from taking in *anything*, even if I know I didn't plow through fourteen thousand calories' worth.

Interestingly enough, my mind goes to the thought that I didn't want to be different from everybody else. Now, I have to peel that apart into three sections. First, I know that my abstinence during the first two hours of the five-year-anniversary party was different from the behavior of most people, but it was invisible and didn't make me stick out in any way. Nobody monitored what anybody else was—or was not—consuming at that party. So that can't matter.

At the birthday dinner party later, we served ourselves buffet style. The dinner consisted of barbecued chicken, lasagna, buttered garlic bread, and tossed green salad. I took only a piece of chicken and some salad. That didn't make me conspicuous, either. (And, now that I recall, it didn't exactly constitute gorging behavior. Where *did* all those calories come from?)

A high-calorie dessert was served at the table, and I certainly could have simply said, No thanks. One other person did, just before mine was served, and it would have been no big deal. But I didn't. Why?

Maybe I just feel sorry for myself in situations like that. (I am probably just feeling sorry for myself this morning too.) Can it be that I haven't yet found the maturity to accept certain necessary and permanent limits on my behavior? Am I ducking what is inevitable, making a big deal out of nothing? Is the answer, *Just shut up and get on with it*?

I know I am facing something like that kind of ultimatum with regard to my back problem. Now that I am out of pain, my doctor has given me an unbelievably complex set of exercises to do every day. Every day. Not almost every day, or every day I can find time for them. Every single day for the rest of my life. If I do them every day, I will have no more back problems. If I do not do them, I will have recurring— and increasingly troublesome—problems. Simple choice, one would think.

I have been doing these exercises for only three days now, and already I am questioning whether I will dedicate a half hour of every day of my life from here on to preventing back problems. It seems, on the face of it, preposterous. Half an hour a day, every day! I'm a busy man. Who can dedicate so much precious time to so invisible a purpose? Especially since I will also be resuming my Nautilus workouts in a couple of weeks, which adds another forty-five minutes or so every other day to the tending of my body.

Is all this really necessary? And now is it also necessary to restrict myself to only those foods and drinks I have thought about in advance, prepared, and packed along with me wherever I go? For the rest of my bloody life?

Can the answer to that be yes?

I really want to know. Is that what this is all about? Is it, *Yes, your body demands this kind of devoted attention that will require—between exercise and food preparation—several hours a day of your faithful attention? During those couple of hours, all other elements of your life take second place. Nothing else should get in your way.*

Are we dealing here with nothing more than the reordering of priorities that is a natural function of aging, of living within a body that is no longer as resilient and tolerant as it once was? I know that elderly people may find it perfectly natural to spend a number of hours a day coping with their physical needs and frailties. Is this just a down payment on that, coming to me at a time when I did not expect it? Am I prematurely frail in some ways I find it hard to accept?

As I write, I sense some of the anger and frustration draining away. I must be on to something here. Even though I wrote the preceding paragraphs in a mood of disbelief, as though the answer could not possibly be yes, I now wonder seriously if the answer is not indeed yes. What began close to sarcasm now quietly becomes truth, truth to be considered soberly and peacefully.

I also feel some kind of invitation emerging too—an invitation to acceptance. Acceptance, resignation, surrender. Whatever emanates from the monks in a monastery—*that* kind of acceptance. The mature, bittersweet realization that there may be other ways for other people, but that only *this* way can be right for me.

I suppose I can make friends with that truth. It just takes some getting used to. It confronts me with much more than setting myself apart as different; that much I have done, both deliberately and unconsciously, my whole life. No, what I have to get used to is what it means about my life.

Such as, I am getting older. The signs of aging that I thought were decades away are already on top of me. My body is in decline.

Such as, I can't do everything I want. The days are not long enough—or numerous enough—to let me pretend that I can do it all and have it all.

I am facing limits.

And I don't like it.

Wow! This is clearly a far cry from losing weight just to look better.

September 25. Weight: 201

Things are getting a little confusing. After what felt like something of a breakthrough in understanding yesterday, I went on to finish the day with a medium-sized binge. How does that figure?

My business partner, Alan, broke out some lovely cashews left over from the party and began eating them at the office, teasing me about how lousy they tasted. I resisted a while, then caved in. I probably ate half a pound of them. Then, at home, after a sensible dinner, I began acting like a real addict: first some crackers and cheese, then a bowl of popcorn, then ice cream; and finally, I was standing in front of the open freezer digging away with a spoon at some rock-hard frozen Cool Whip, for God's sake.

Ordinarily, I would feel a little panicked at this experience, but I think I know what is going on. First, I think I am responding physiologically to the remaining aftereffects of alcohol. Both Saturday and Sunday, I indulged in some wine and champagne, and the stuff is simply deadly for me. I *cannot* let it into my system without my appetite getting knocked out of kilter.

Second, I think in some ways I was reacting to the understanding I reached yesterday. I believe I touched a nerve that is a central part of the experiment at this point, and my eating yesterday felt like a last little gasp of resistance, a childish thumbing my nose at the future I know I must accept.

There was yet another factor, too, perhaps—health. I live with nagging fear that my extra weight really will damage my health; certainly all the statistics point that way. The kinds of risks are just the kind that killed my father—high blood pressure and coronary heart disease.

By coincidence, I had an insurance physical yesterday afternoon. My blood pressure was boringly normal. That was anything but boring for me, though, and I felt in very high spirits the rest of the afternoon. I guess I worry about it much, much more than I have realized.

Wait! I am suddenly putting two and two together. *Before* I had my physical, I resisted the cashews with real discipline; *after* the exam, I raided the jar. The news of my excellent blood pressure obviously lifted some of the fear that motivates my discipline and released me to indulge.

So I guess my worries about health consequences play more of a role than I realized. I remember dismissing them as unimportant in the early pages of this experiment; now, I think I'd better spend some time one of these days looking at them more closely.

I say "one of these days" because I am pressed for time today. I have a special event coming up: my portrait sitting. Yes, today is the day. At 1:00 this afternoon I will be in a nearby village at the studio of (heaven help me) Brooke Shields' portrait artist.

I don't have an expert perspective on what the differences are between my body and Brooke's, but poor Pat Hamm will know shortly. I hope she's up to it.

September 27. Weight: 198½

I didn't get back to the typewriter yesterday evening—or at all yesterday—thanks to an out-of-town trip. But I do want to reach back to the unfinished day and talk about my visit to the artist.

It had taken me no small amount of effort to get up enough courage to go through with this brilliant idea. And I felt plenty hesitant as I prepared to leave the house that morning. What should I take to wear, for instance. I wanted to wear something that would reveal my physique, of course, and yet something that could add to the meaning of it all. I settled on a pair of tennis shorts, without a shirt. Tennis is my favorite sport, and when my back isn't killing me, I try to play several times a week. It is the only time when I am particularly aware that my body is at odds with the requirements of both society and the task at hand.

I selected a pair of tennis shorts, a pair that are very tight on me right now. I might as well have the full effect of my bulges.

I found my way to her studio. She was everything I hoped for: warm, direct, friendly, interested, understanding. We spent a lively half hour swapping tales of our struggle with weight, comparing attempts to diet, and finding a wider range of shared interests.

I took off my shirt and made a conscious decision not to suck in my gut. Do you know how hard it is to let it all hang out when you know someone—especially a woman—is studying you? When someone is carefully tracing every inch of your body with their eyes, studying and thinking and remembering and imagining? To let every single muscle relax and let every wave of flesh settle into whatever contour gravity dictates? Without even slightly tensing your stomach muscles or adjusting your posture to improve the picture just a bit?

It is not easy. I tried, but even now I am not sure I wasn't fudging.

No matter. What I saw in the mirror, and she with her eyes and mind's eye, seemed plenty bad enough.

This is important. I really mean bad. What I saw when I took my shirt off and looked in the mirror was pretty objectionable. Simply unattractive.

I would have chalked it up to self-consciousness, with good reason, since I was about to be ogled by a pro. But it went beyond that, I think. I think I was making an aesthetic judgment. I think I was saying *a human body shaped this way doesn't look too hot. Not my body, necessarily, but any body.*

For whatever reason, seeing myself in the mirrors at Pat Hamm's studio gave me, for the first time, an objective picture of my body and an objective opinion about it, and I was not happy about it. Perhaps the meaning will become clear later on.

Well, fortunately, I didn't have to stand very long before Pat with my shorts straining to contain overstuffed hips and buttocks while folds of fat drooped in ripples down my front side. She got out a camera and took a number of shots of me—long range, close up, front, side, rear. Black-and-white photos. Like a police officer takes at the scene of a crime or a coroner takes in a morgue. Harsh studies of one man's anatomy.

When she was satisfied (with her photography, that is), she told me I could go. She said she had all she needed to work from and would call me in a couple of weeks when she finished my pair of portraits: one just the way I am today, and one showing me about forty pounds lighter.

I don't want to see the first one, but I am passionately interested in the other. Could it hold the key to success?

October 2. Weight: 201½

It may be time to abandon this exercise. So far it has accomplished exactly nothing. I have not lost weight. I do not have any greater understanding of why I am not slim.

But I keep at it.

Why?

I sit here this morning and can't think of a single reason. I feel doomed by my body's chemistry, or my psychology, or whatever, to a life of fatness. I cannot devote my whole damned life to scientifically researching the complexities of the matter.

Yet, I'll probably mush on ahead with it anyhow. I will tire of the subject soon enough, but I haven't yet. I keep stumbling onto fresh ideas to respond to, and perhaps some combination of them will prove effective at breaking me out of the quicksand this experiment is stuck in now.

A new notion came at me out of the TV today in a locally produced special on the problem of obesity. It hit me hard. Very hard. Fat people, according to this report, may very well require fewer calories than thin people to fuel their bodies. Due to some perverse *efficiency* in the way we utilize calories, it appears that fewer calories are needed to run the machinery—and the rest are stored as fat. So if, for example, my lean business partner and I eat exactly the same amount, he might not add an ounce of flesh to his frame, and I might add another ripple round my waist.

I don't quite know why this had such an impact on me, but it did. It may explain for the first time why my older brother stayed skinny while packing away day in and day out what I was sure were more calories than I did. But all I have ever heard was that either I must eat more when others weren't around, or people who aren't fat must eat less when I wasn't around. Or something. Something that always made it my *fault* that slim people were slim and I wasn't.

This report may help me get past blaming myself and beating myself up about this all the time. Maybe I can graduate from being so damned defensive about it. The fact is, it *is* a physiological and psychological condition; we humans are a blend of mind and body, fully integrated, and each part interacts seamlessly with the other. It is of limited value to say the problem is more one than the other. But it may be of some value. And if it turns out that our metabolism creates the condition that creates the psychology, at least that provides some release from the constant guilt and doubt about whether I "should" be able to do something more about it than I am.

That would be a big step forward: reduce the immediate task to one of physiology only. Accept that my body needs less food than most of the bodies around me. Accept that I will always have to restrict my food intake—because that is what my particular body requires. Accept that some of the pleasures of bygone eating and drinking are indeed gone forever. Accept a simple fact, a snapshot of reality that will forever change my intake patterns. Period. No psychologizing. No resentfulness. No muttering about societal standards of slimness. Just eat less because my body requires less.

I wish it could be as easy as it sounds.

October 10. Weight: 201

I just got my portrait—a glimpse of the future Eliot. It leaves me both speechless and babbling. I don't know where to begin, except by shouting out that I may have stumbled onto something really incredible! Whatever inspired me to do this was nothing short of miraculous.

The impact is astounding. Nothing has ever hit me quite like this. I am reeling, astonished, enchanted, gratified, thrilled. Thrilled! That captures a lot of it. It takes me where I have never been before and excites me about being there. Thrilling. Magical, even.

When Pat called the day before yesterday to say it was ready, I felt indifferent. For a week or more, I had lost all heart for the experiment, discouraged over my lack of progress in losing weight, discouraged by my discouragement. As a result, I hadn't written for a week and had eaten carelessly, even piggishly. My weight leaped to 205 as of day before yesterday—precisely where it was when I began. I agreed without enthusiasm to an appointment with Pat last evening to pick up my portraits and arrived with few expectations beyond a mild curiosity.

What I found there knocked me off my feet. Taped to the wall were the two charcoal portraits. On the left, a dazzling, accurate picture of me exactly as I know myself now. It was the Eliot I face in the mirror every day, recreated with astonishing skill. My eyes went first to the face and I found myself there. Then, they slid quickly to the sagging bulges around my hips and back up slightly to my breasts. Yes, this is precisely the body I wear. I felt no emotion or judgment, just an affirmation that this is a guy I know and like and live with. The portrait confirmed beyond a doubt that Pat is an immensely gifted artist who really captured all of who I know I am.

In practically the same instant, my eyes were drawn to the portrait on the right. There stood a trim and attractive picture of me. The "me" is crucial to understand. It was *me*. Not a version of me or a speculation of me or an idealized dream of me. It was *me!* I knew that guy too. He was real and possible. He was someone I already knew and liked. I *knew* him. There was a real link between the two—the one on the right was the same as the one on the left, just shaped differently, and frankly, more attractive.

He looked friendly, the way I think of myself. This surprised me, because I associate leanness with a certain severity. I liked that he looked so friendly. His tennis shorts fit. There were no sideways wrinkles of the tension between fabric and flesh. He looked comfortable. He looked at home in his lean body. I knew this guy and liked him.

I knew I could love him as much as I love the guy on the left.

What was more important, I knew in an instant that I could go to the guy on the right without condemning the guy on the left. It was all so simple. Eliot could look one way or the other. Period. Either way, Eliot was still Eliot.

Suddenly, I felt no need to defend the fat Eliot or to protect him by declaring our lifelong friendship and mutual suffering. Everything was so purely objective. Eliot can look either way. It is still Eliot, and there is a clear choice that doesn't cost anything in terms of allegiance, loyalty, continuity of identify. *My identity can survive the transition from one body shape to the other.* That is the heart of it. That is what this whole portrait thing proved.

To be Eliot, I do not *have* to be one way or the other.

I have a choice. A clear, simple, pure choice. Astonishingly, I never knew that before.

I never knew that before.

It is hard to imagine, but profoundly true. Until I saw the two portraits of me, I never knew I could be either way and still be *me*.

It is impossible to overestimate the potential power of knowing this. I say "potential" because I have no way of knowing what I will in fact do with the power. I could walk away from it and stay the way I am, or I could energize myself with it and move toward the Eliot on the right.

But I do not doubt one thing: the power is there, and I am the one responsible for using it or not. I am no longer a psychological prisoner of the familiar fat Eliot, paralyzed by the fear of an unknown and unknowable future Eliot. I *know* this future Eliot now and I like him, trust him, could be very good friends with him forever.

The portrait gives me a new baseline, *an alternative for what is normal* for myself. That's it. A new standard of normal. I am not stuck with just one image by which to keep in touch with myself. Now, I have another image that is equally real, true, approachable, available.

There is incredible power here, power to release me from a fierce bondage to one single image of Eliot. Power to transform my past loyalty to a *shape* into a new loyalty to a *person*. I am less the shape than I could ever have imagined. I am contained in the shape, and it forms a major part of my concept of myself, but *I am not the shape*. I am the person inside the shape. I am the person inside the shape. I am the person *inside* the shape.

That person can take on a new shape. That person already *has* taken on a new shape, through the portrait. *He already exists!* That is the miracle! The trim, solid Eliot already exists. My task is simply to make him real, to uncover him. I just can't begin to get a handle on the power of this event.

October 12. Weight: 199¼

I continue to be amazed at the detachment and objectivity I feel about weight and shape right now. I saw a man who looks like I do currently, and a curious reaction ran through my head. With a mental shrug I thought, *Well, sure, a person can look like that if he or she chooses to. It's one way.*

That's the power of it: being fat is just one way to be, no more or less inevitable than any other choice. That's all. Now I can see another way to be, and it has the power to draw me to it.

I have never experienced a *choice* before. Everything before has been in reaction to one situation, struggling with a lifetime of being fat. I have focussed everything on that—hating it, fighting it, surrendering to it, hating myself for surrendering to it. But it dominated everything.

But now it is an also-ran, just one possibility among others. Choose, Eliot, now that you can see what your choices are. You are not a prisoner of what is, struggling to make it slightly more tolerable. You have a brand new possibility that the portrait is making real and reachable.

I am frustrated trying to fully express how totally different this situation is. Let me try another angle: what I have now is *a goal that is expressed as me, not as the absence of a certain number of pounds.* I look at the portrait of the trim Eliot, and it shapes my every thought and feeling about the subject. I want to be *that* Eliot. By contrast, I do not want to lose ten or twenty or thirty pounds; I want to be *that* Eliot. I like him!

How different—utterly different—that is from *disliking this* Eliot. If all you have going for you is the desire to escape who you are and wander into the future as some unknown person you are not now—that is all but impossible, at least for me. But the miracle of the portrait is that I am able to move *toward* someone I know and like, someone who is me already, a different and maybe a better me, a me I want to make real and permanent.

The power of the miracle works in funny ways on a day-to-day basis too. Last night, for example, I spent the evening with friends watching the presidential debates. Naturally our hosts served dessert. I ignored it.

Now, the key word is *ignored.* I did not, by contrast, "resist" it, or "overcome the temptation" or anything else. I ignored it. And I think I know why. The very instant it appeared, any temptation to eat it was cut short by a strong, quiet voice in my mind saying, *That is not the way to the goal.*

The goal, again. The power of the goal. The magnetic attraction of the goal. The clear, real, reachable goal. It sounds so simple, but it never existed before. No *goal* ever existed before. All that existed was a combination of dissatisfaction with my self—the only self I thought existed—and a wishful dream about some other person I might become if I were somehow different. That is not a goal. (Neither is some number of pounds to be lost; I mean, how can something that *disappears* be a goal?)

My new thinking changes the way I see my current shape: it seems to be a temporary thing, not my permanent fate. When I glimpse my body now in the mirror, my reaction is profoundly different from just a couple of days ago. For years—for a lifetime—I have had one of two reactions. About half the time, I felt disgust and instantly would attack myself: *You stupid slob, how can you let yourself look that way!* I would continue the battering until I couldn't stand it any more and needed relief. The other half, I would speak to myself a little line of encouragement: *Not too bad. Not too bad.* My urge was to make it O.K., to see myself within a range of normality that, while admittedly on the plump side, still did not deserve to be the object of my own—or anyone else's—negative judgment.

Now my reaction is totally different. I mentally shrug and pass my current shape off as outmoded.

A shrug. Indifferent. I can see now, by contrast, how much of my inner dialogue has been shaped either in reaction against, or in desperate affirmation of, my fat body.

I realize that the accuracy of the portrait has a lot to do with its power. I do not want to give up who I am. And the accuracy of the image reassures me that I will continue to be this me, just packaged a bit differently.

With the benefit of a clear alternative, I can now see that my body image is not *me*; now, my body shape is just *part* of me. Changing it no longer seems like changing the underlying reality of me. It just seems like changing my shape, that's all. My shape just doesn't seem to be all that big a deal, all that important and central an element in my identity. It seems more like an accessory, something that comes along with the rest of me, but in no way defines or determines anything more important. It can be shaped this way or that way, round or slim, soft or hard. Options. Choices. Alternatives. Like so many body styles and colors on automobiles. Pay your nickel and take your choice.

October 25. Weight: 204

I am losing it.

Not the weight. God knows, not the weight. I have gained almost five pounds in the last five days.

I am losing the effects of the portrait. I am losing the power of it, the magic of it. After less than two weeks, I am losing my grasp of all it seemed to be bringing out in me. I reread what I wrote, and I recall what I felt during those heady days after I got it—and still I can't keep it alive. It skitters away in glittering, elusive fragments I can't catch. I am struggling now, not to recover it but simply to keep from skidding into a depression over the loss.

How cruel. To be lifted so high and then dropped so hard. Where did it *go?* Where does an infatuation go when the thrill wears off?

I've been here before and I shudder to remember. I don't think I can stand going through another battering, being slammed from emotional high to devastating low, from success to disaster, from shouting with glee to wallowing in despair. This has been going on my whole damned life!

Back when I was fifteen, when I had the outburst with my parents and screamed for help with my fatness, they responded in the only way they knew how, I suppose. They sent me to a doctor. And he responded in what was probably the only way he knew.

He put me on Dexedrine pills. I don't blame the doctor. I'm sure all the medical literature of the day said the same thing—put the fat folks on Dexedrine. It'll kill their appetites. It wasn't until some years later that these so-called diet pills were revealed as the equivalent of the drug speed, and the high they created came to be abused by druggies from coast to coast.

Well, Dexedrine certainly did kill the appetite, no question about that. But that wasn't all it did, of course. As is well known now, these damned pills can make a person crazy. And they nearly did. For my last two years of high school, I was high as a kite one minute, devastated and fatigued the next. Dexedrine whipsawed me up and down, back and forth, from manic bliss in which food didn't even exist for me, to dark exhaustion in which no amount of food was enough to fill me and still me.

Yet, pills were the only game in town, and I played—off and on—until I graduated. I say "off and on" because I had to quit taking them from time to time; they were devastating. So when I could stand them, I took them and didn't eat. When I had to have some relief from Dexedrine burnout, I laid off for a while—with predictable results. Deep exhaustion, depression, isolation, renewed binges. Dexedrine or too much food—I was numbed out on one or the other all the time.

The constant turmoil between highs and lows left me utterly in social limbo. I didn't know whether I was the coolest dude on the block or the creepiest slob in the county. One thing I was sure of all the time: I was saddled with an ugly body.

So I didn't date much in high school because I didn't feel attractive. I couldn't stand the thought of being rejected if I asked someone for a date, and whatever dates I did have were carefully arranged and negotiated through third parties, who would feel out my hoped-for date's attitude toward me. I wound up having some good times with a few girls, but never felt free to play the field. I lived in fear of making an advance and getting a sarcastic reply that would assail me for being a fat boy.

Although I was an accepted member of a popular gang of kids, I was always on the fringe of it—partly because of my fat. I avoided many of the gatherings—poolside, at the beach, waterskiing—where too much of me would be on display. That eliminated a lot of social contact.

So I choked down as much Dexedrine as I could to try to make myself look—or feel—attractive enough to risk asking girls for dates. But then I would have to bail out from time to time, to get relief from the battering of the dope.

The power of Dexedrine being what it is, I wound up losing more than I gained and graduated from high school at a relatively trim 175 pounds. I headed off for college on the wings of unaccustomed confidence. I actually felt pretty good about myself.

Of course, it didn't take long for me to bulk up again. When the pressures of college hit—social pressures, academic pressures, self-inflicted pressures—I did what I have always done.

I ate.

No, I *over*ate. *That* is what I really did. And I really did it some more.

By now, beer was of course a staple "food." Not that it hadn't been in high school—but the difference was its availability. I kept my own refrigerator well stocked, the fraternity house usually had a keg on ice, and friends' cars frequently toted ice chests with a few six packs chilling just for emergencies. I guzzled plenty, with all the lack of restraint that by now was a dominant part of my behavior. The thought of returning to popping Dexedrine pills was too awful to consider. My body screamed *no!* and I agreed.

So I spent plenty of private hours stuffing my face to avoid facing the rest of my life. In a matter of months, I managed to binge my way back to a blubbery two hundred pounds or so—enough to make me avoid the waterskiing outings at the lake that were such a regular part of our college social life. After the first time waterskiing with my college gang, I couldn't bear the thought of a repeat.

What was wrong with the first time? Just two things: I was the only one in the party who couldn't get the waterskiing life belt around my waist and had to wear a bulky orange Coast Guard surplus life preserver. And I was the only one the boat couldn't pull out of the water, powered as it was with but a thirty-five-horsepower engine that was totally overmatched by the combination of my weight and the resistance of the bulky life preserver. So, as a reminder, I got to spend the rest of the afternoon being skipped over each time my turn came.

Snow skiing was also a part of my classmates' social activities—but not mine. Since few of us had much money, there was a lot of borrowing of clothes back and forth, especially expensive specialty items like ski pants. Snow skiing is one of those sports a person really needs the right equipment for, and I never could afford items for rarely occurring events—my own water ski belt or ski pants. So mostly I avoided them, isolating myself while others were doing group events together.

But there came a time when I simply had to have some ski pants for the weekend: I was chairman of our fraternity's annual ski festival. Surely, the chairman had to dress the part even if he were no great shakes on the slopes. So I borrowed a pair of expensive new ski pants from a friend—they were the first stretch fabric pants on the market, and I was sure I could somehow squeeze into them.

I did (although I shudder to think what I must have looked like). But at a big party on the very first night of the three-day festival, I bent over and split the pants from stem to stern, right up the crotch. They didn't just slip a stitch or two. Oh, no. These were stretch pants, stretched to the limit. They were under serious pressure and so when they went, they really went. Pow! The whole crotch exploded—from belt line in the rear to bottom of the fly in the front. Pow! All of a sudden, I was standing there in two leggings and a loincloth.

Of course, those pants were all I had brought to wear. So eager was I to be accepted for my real-skier attire, I had given no thought whatsoever to bringing along any alternatives—

any of my own nonskier pants that, although uncool, at least fit me.

I was two hundred miles from home with my butt hanging out of a pair of very expensive pants—someone else's very expensive pants—that were now reduced to rags. This was not a happy moment. Faced with the prospect of three days wearing a sweater tied around my waist to cover my butt or going home for a pair of pants, I chose the all-night drive to my house and back. I got back to the resort by dawn and spent the next two days feeling foolishly out of place in Levi's. When I wasn't feeling foolish, I was worrying myself sick about where I'd ever get the money to buy my friend a new pair of ski pants.

But even that kind of experience couldn't get me back onto Dexedrine. I knew its magic was treachery and whatever high it gave me, whatever weight loss it enabled, I would pay dearly in the end.

And now, I think I am paying dearly again. I think I set myself up for another big fall, from the high of the portrait to the reality of my own sick instincts to eat and overeat and overeat some more. I thought I had invented the most powerful medicine of all time, one that would cure this sickness forever.

But the surge of new hope and energy provided by the portrait of a slim Eliot has proved short-lived, unmasked as the latest in my lifelong series of quick fixes. I'm afraid it has turned out to be a sort of psychological crash diet that, like all crash diets, has a savage undertow lurking just beneath the first wave of success.

And so the hope and energy are drifting away, like a lover grown indifferent without knowing quite why. Who knows why? I certainly don't, but I know that within just a few days the magic is simply gone.

As the magic peters out, the backlash seems even more depressing than usual, because the high has been so much higher and seemed so much purer and truer than anything I had experienced before. I had felt so close, so close to having a breakthrough that would fix everything for me.

Fat chance.

Unless something more happens for me than happened when I looked at that portrait a few minutes ago, the sickness is on the rise again—and I am on my way back down. And I am scared, really scared, about how low low will be this time.

November 1. Weight: 205

Whatever I had, I don't have it anymore. The portrait mocks me when I look at it. The scale mocks me when I stand on it. So I have ignored the portrait and the scales and the writing for a week. I wouldn't be sitting here this morning if I could think of anything better to do.

But something has nudged me over here to my typewriter, to keep pecking away just a bit longer. I know that I am not going to win at this experiment. That is quite evident now. No, wait. What I mean is that I am not going to escape a lifetime of being fat. I can still win at this experiment, however, if only I can understand what happened, understand why it is all turning out this way.

Then, at least, I can live out my days knowing that I did give it my best shot. I will be able to live free of the poisonous thought that it could have been different for me if only I had tried harder. I have tried as hard as I know how. God, what more could anybody ask from me? I am wrung out from the effort. I have given it *everything* I have to give. I just don't know how to think more creatively or push harder or probe more intensely than this. What the hell else could I have done anyhow?

So I need to write a bit more, to try to clarify my final understanding and bring this exercise to a decent close. I don't have much heart for the task, but I know it's important and I'll persevere somehow.

Let's see. What's going on in my life that relates to all this? Exercise. That, anyhow, is on the upswing. I have decided to take some tennis lessons, to lift the level of my game a notch or two. I have played since I was twelve, and my game is fairly good for a weekend player. But my son, now sixteen, has become such a strong player that I am having a hard time staying on the court with him. Not that I am out to beat him; I can see the writing on *that* wall very clearly. He plays competitively on his school team and has been too good for me for a year or two, and I'll probably never win another set from him. But I do want us to be able to enjoy each other on the court, and if the gap between us gets too large, I won't be any fun for him to play. That would be a real loss for me, not getting to play together. As his life becomes ever more independent, I'd like some things to endure as ties between us.

So I signed up for lessons with his private coach, a hotshot pro. He teaches a crop of strong young turks like my son who are all power and speed and killer instinct. He has me out there hitting with them. So far, my son doesn't seem to be embarrassed at the sight of his flabby father. I suppose my tennis skills, including a few shots the younger guys haven't developed yet, help offset my unathletic appearance and give him something to respect. The workouts are ferocious, and it is clear that my body is no longer equal to the punishment these sixteen to twenty year olds are putting themselves through. I'll have to set some limits or be in trouble before long.

But I can feel a rising resistance to asking for any special consideration. I have a lifetime of humiliation at the hands of coaches and in the eyes of athletes, and I want to avoid special treatment come hell or high water.

The diet may not have worked, and the portrait may not have been the magic solution, but I still have *some* dignity.

November 26. Weight: 211

Where do you begin, when you are at the end?

I feel like I am at the end and I don't expect any news to the contrary. For almost a week now, I have been flat on my bed, absolutely unable to move. It's my back. My back is all but destroyed, thanks to the idiotic workouts I put myself through with the cream of the local tennis talent. Day after punishing day, I did my damnedest to push myself to a higher level of conditioning, of performance, of results on the court. I was making real progress too. In just three weeks of daily workouts, my game was much stronger, and I was holding my own with players I couldn't have touched a year ago.

Then one morning I couldn't get out of bed. Period. When I awoke I couldn't move. The slightest effort to roll over or to sit up stabbed me with terrible, terrible pain in my lower back. I was—and still am—almost completely paralyzed. I have been this way for a week now and my life is a wreck.

I am unable to get to my office, of course. I conduct what little business I can over the phone, but the pain saps my energy, my intellect, and my spirit. I have had to cancel a long-planned family vacation, and it will be weeks before I am able to function at anything like normal. I am letting down my family, my partner, and God only knows who else.

And I am doing what I always do when I am in pain. I am eating—what else?

I am stretched out on the sofa in our living room all day long, all by myself. Trish is off at work, the kids are at school, and I am angry, bored, and frustrated. I am in no mood to think about counting calories or about messing with that portrait or anything else remotely connected with my fatness.

And so my fatness is growing. Alarmingly.

My weight is 211 pounds today—within four pounds of my all-time top weight, and way the hell beyond what is reasonable for my body. And, of course, the extra weight is contributing substantially to the pain in my back and hampering my healing.

I am bouncing back and forth between alarm and indifference, between agitated anxiety and depressed unconcern, between *You've got to do something!* and *Who gives a shit?*

When I am agitated about it, I really panic. I know now that my eating is totally out of control. I feel like I am watching a forest fire racing across a mountainside, powering and feeding itself on the fierce winds created by its own heat. Using its own heat to prepare everything in its path for destruction, the fire sears new timbers to the combustion point long before the flames actually arrive. I am being eaten alive by the madness of my own eating, and I am no more able to stop it than I could halt a fire exploding through forests.

I am at the mercy of my eating now and I am quite afraid it is going to kill me. No, I am quite *certain* it is going to kill me. I know how vulnerable I am to diseases associated with obesity, and I have every reason to believe they will visit and destroy me as surely as the sun will rise. The only question left for me is not whether but when.

There is one other question: will I resist or welcome them?

Because when I am not agitated, when I don't give a damn, I realize I am tired of this struggle. I really am. I have put into it everything I had and now I am empty. I have nothing to show for it but proof of my failure, a pair of charcoal portraits depicting the inevitable and the impossible, a shredded lower back stabbing me with terrible pain, and the prospect of another so-called friend telling me someday how rotten I look and how glad he is not to look like me. I can hardly wait.

That's all I can manage for today.

December 9. Weight: 216

I hit a new high and a new low today.

The new high is my weight. In the last five weeks I have gained eleven pounds. I have never weighed 216 before. I am not surprised, though, that I weigh 216 now. Ever since Thanksgiving two weeks ago, the house has been filled with all kinds of goodies, and I have had nothing better to do all day than to struggle up from the living room sofa, hobble out to the pantry, and stuff my face. Cold stuffing and hot gravy. Pumpkin pie with whipped cream. Pumpkin pie with vanilla ice cream. Pumpkin ice cream with pumpkin pie. Shortbread. Mixed nuts. Macadamia nuts. Fresh home-baked bread with butter.

The food calls to me. I lie on the sofa and hear it calling from the pantry. The food knows I know it's there, waiting for me. It knows that I will come for it, sooner or later. *Why not sooner, then, Eliot?* O.K.

I cannot stop. I am totally unable to stop the impulse to eat. I am going to eat myself to death. What do I mean, "going to"?! I *am* eating myself to death.

I found that out officially today. That is my new low. I went to the doctor and learned, among other things, that my blood pressure has shot through the roof. After decades of readings at the borderline between safe and dangerous, I am now certifiably at risk—huge risk—with readings *way* over the limits. I am now on big-time medication, beta-blockers and all that. These are medicines that reach deep into body systems and screw up a lot of things in an effort to keep the heart working. They have side effects for lots of people, I understand, including diminishing sex drive and who knows what else—all to defend my heart from the impact of my fat.

Never mind trying just to stave off a heart attack; my doctor says I am a "great" candidate for a stroke. That is a charming prospect that never entered my mind before today. I have had fantasies of a heart attack, of course—a blinding flash of pain that drops me in my tracks and kills me outright, like it did my father.

But a *stroke?* At my age? No explosive heart attack to end it all, with grieving widow and other survivors covered by life insurance to tend to their material needs. A stroke, for God's sake? Me, at my age, some kind of basket case stretched out here on the sofa *forever?* Struggling to make myself understood, struggling to understand others, wobbly of mind and body?

I am desperate. I am dying, and I don't know how to stop dying. I know that I will continue to gain weight. No question about that. And my doctor will continue to feed me whatever medicines he has to cope with the destruction of my body systems. But it's only a matter of time now. And I don't know what to do about it.

January 15. Weight: 222

I haven't written for five weeks. Last time I wrote, I had hit a new high (in weight) and a new low (in hope for the future). Impossible though it seems, both positions have worsened. My weight today is astounding: 222 pounds. I went out yesterday and bought a pair of pants with a forty-two-inch waist because I cannot fit into any other clothes I own.

If I hadn't been so desperate, I would have been humiliated. But an air of unreality sets in at this stage, as though I'm moving in slow motion through somebody else's life. I simply needed some pants that would reach around my belly and went out and bought them. No emotion whatsoever.

I wish I thought this represented a new level of "acceptance"—that serene attitude I promised myself so long ago when I began this whole damned experiment. I would take that as a reasonable outcome if it proved that I couldn't achieve a permanent weight loss. But how can you accept a condition you know is just a few steps removed from the end of your life when you don't have to be there?

I know, of course, that the end of my life is somewhere over a fairly near horizon. I don't want that, but I am not stupid either: someone who is gaining weight the way I am will not take long to overwhelm his body's ability to cope. Even though I can't imagine that I will continue to gain at the rate I have lately (almost five pounds per month for four months), I know beyond a doubt that I will continue to gain something. Even a pound or two every month or two will have me over 250 in no time, with 300 in range within a few years.

And I am helpless to stop it. I don't give a damn what people think or say—"No, no! You're not helpless! Just try again! Try harder! Wait: there's a great new diet that's guaranteed to work!"—I know better now.

What I can see now is that I have been an uncontrolled eater all my life—not just on the occasional binges that made an unwelcome blip on the scale. The *effects* of my overeating were masked all these years by my energetic exercise program. What I am now realizing, with shocking clarity, is that I have always burned off the worst of the excess eating with my daily running, my tennis, and my other activities.

But suddenly, paralyzed with a bad back and stripped of the ability to burn off the massive amounts of extra food that I have *habitually* stuffed away, I see the future. I won't always be able to burn off unneeded food that way, and I can't ever seem to stop eating unneeded food. That leaves me with only one clear, certain future: more weight and more weight and more weight—until my systems collapse and either take me out quickly, with the big heart attack, or reduce me to rubble through a stroke.

I am desperate.

And I take my desperation to be a good sign. I think it means I want to live.

Now, I have to find a way to act on my instinct.

January 17. Weight: 222

I really am desperate and I am ready to try anything. I am not ready to pack it in, to call it quits on my life. I can live with being fat, but I can't live as a walking dead man. I will buy myself a wardrobe of forty-two-inch pants if I must, and I will struggle to control my eating as best I can, and I will work hard to rehabilitate my back so I can resume some calorie-burning exercise as soon as possible. All that I can and will do.

But I have to do something more. I am not sure what, but I think it has to do with understanding how this uncontrolled overeating has gotten such an upper hand.

I have tried most of the published diet programs and joined most of the commercial diet organizations—Weight Watchers, Diet Center, Lean Line, and all that. I was a star pupil: paid my money, lost my weight, went away and regained it. They were only too willing to welcome me back for another round, of course. There has to be a better way. That's why I began this experiment in the first place. But clearly *that* isn't the way, either.

I know of only one more possibility.

So tomorrow I am going to a meeting I heard about. It is a group called Overeaters Anonymous. I think it's like Alcoholics Anonymous, but for people who overeat instead of overdrink.

I first heard about Overeaters Anonymous four or five years ago from a person whose advice I did not want—about anything, let alone my weight. So I promptly stashed the name and idea in my mental dead letter file. It must have been buried very, very deep, because in subsequent years I worked professionally with a client whose activities repeatedly brought me into contact with Alcoholics Anonymous and with alcoholism treatment programs. I remember being struck, forcefully, at how much the symptoms of alcoholism resembled my experience with food. I even mentioned that to my client at the time and wondered out loud if there shouldn't be a similar organization for people who abuse food instead of alcohol.

I guess it is a measure of how screwed up I am that I could think and say that, even while keeping buried my knowledge that just such an organization already does exist.

Anyhow, the name came back to me last night, absolutely out of the blue. I wasn't even thinking (consciously) about my problem (although I continue to stew in my desperation). But there it was: "Overeaters Anonymous" floating across my mind.

I looked it up in the phone book. There was a phone number that I wrote down, but didn't call right away. I thought about it for a while, snatched a few handsful of nuts, and eventually got up the nerve to dial the number. I reached a woman named Lydia. When I asked about the organization, she said

I should just go to a meeting to find out about it. Apparently, there are meetings all over the place, all the time. She told me of three within five minutes' drive of my house. One of them is tomorrow morning, Saturday, at 10:30. I'll be there.

III

I believe I have found my home.

January 18. Weight: 222

I have just returned from the Overeaters Anonymous meeting, and I am overcome. I don't know quite where to begin—with a description of the meeting itself or with an attempt to describe what I think it means to me.

But what is most important is this: I believe I have found my home.

I do not use the word *home* loosely. My family and our home is the very heart and soul of my life. I suppose I idolize it in many ways. So when I use the word *home* to describe how I felt at that meeting, I am reaching for the most important, meaningful, satisfying word in my entire vocabulary. Home is where I feel total acceptance and know I am loved no matter what.

I think this Overeaters Anonymous is the same kind of place.

I can also say that I wept through most of the meeting, if that provides a snapshot of what it was like for me.

I'd better go back to the start. I arrived at the meeting just as it was beginning, down in the basement conference room of a small hospital in our town. When I first walked through the door to the meeting room, I was sure the woman on the phone had given me wrong directions. I expected to see the same kind of crew I was used to seeing at Weight Watchers or wherever—most of them between plump and fat, with a few truly obese people as well.

But I looked across this room at a long table full of people, twenty or so in all, who were mostly well-proportioned; many of them were truly slender and only a couple were obviously fat. My sense of confusion must have shown on my face as I hesitated at the doorway.

"May I help you?" someone asked. "If you are looking for Overeaters Anonymous, this is the right place."

This is the right place. No truer words were ever spoken.

The meeting got under way with the leader introducing herself: "I am Helen and I am a compulsive overeater." The words *compulsive overeater* stunned me and thrilled me. I had never heard the term before, but I knew *exactly* what it meant. I thought, *My God, that's what I am—a compulsive overeater!*

I can't tell you what it meant to have a real name to describe me; it meant that whatever I am, it is somehow known, knowable, understandable. If you can at least name it, it seems like you can also begin to cope with it.

And share it! I am one and so is she! And so (I was to discover) is everyone else in the room. Throughout the meeting, as various people read passages from books or shared their thoughts, each would introduce himself or herself with the same words—"I am so-and-so and I am a compulsive overeater." The bond between them was warmer, closer, more *important* somehow than anything I have experienced between people who are not blood relatives. It felt like Christmas Eve at our house.

In that meeting, I felt relief that was deep and total. Imagine, hearing those words and being surrounded by all these people who were *declaring* what I have spent my life *hiding.* The nastiest secret of my life, my insane passion for overeating—my *compulsion* to overeat—the very thing I have exhausted myself trying to conceal, was no secret here. No secret, no embarrassment, no shame. Just the opposite! It was the very bond between them all. Between *us* all.

I was so overcome with deep, deep waves of relief that I struggle to recall and describe with any real accuracy what happened during the rest of the meeting. They read some passages from a book, took a few minutes to write individual reflections on what was read, and then shared some painful and not-so-painful experiences with compulsive overeating that sounded like pages out of my own life. Nobody asked me anything or asked anything of me. I just sat and listened. And as I listened to each member of the group introduce himself or herself as a "compulsive overeater" and describe hurtful incidents from their lives as fat people and describe their self-destructive behavior as food addicts, I knew I was home. I know that is a strange word to keep using—*home*—but it is the only one that will do for me. I sat in my chair and said nothing. I just took it all in, and wept quietly.

I wept with relief, because for the first time in my entire life I was among people who *understood*. They understood it *all*—the pain I had suffered, the helplessness that destroyed my self-esteem, the power that food possessed over me. My whole life, I have felt so alone and so ashamed. I have been *humiliated* by food. Dumb, lifeless, mindless food has some-how taken me prisoner and made a fool of me, despite my best efforts. What kind of worthless jerk does that make me, anyhow? I have been certain that, because I was powerless over food, only I could be so weak and such a failure and feel so unlovable.

And now here I was surrounded by fifteen or twenty decent, warm, caring people describing days out of my life that they had lived too. There was no shame among them. They talked calmly and respectfully about the condition they—we—all suffer together. They call it a "disease" and that sounds right to me. They freely admitted—no, they really *insisted* on admitting—they were utterly powerless over food and that without help, they could not cope by themselves with its le-thal attraction.

There was another theme repeated in what they read and said. They insisted on acknowledging that, even though they mostly appeared well-proportioned and seemed to be in control of their eating, none of them were ever "cured" of this disease. The most they hoped and prayed for was a borrowed power that would help them cope with it "one day at a time." (I think this is an AA phrase too.)

As the meeting progressed, so did I. Deeper and deeper, the relief spread through me. Warmly, tenderly, relief flowed into dark places, where my scared feelings of humiliation were hiding, and comforted them. It spread, too, into the overheated centers in my mind where, for years, my stressed-out mental machinery has spun madly in a losing effort to explain away my eating behavior. I could feel an unwinding, a relaxing, a quieting I have never known before.

And relief worked its way toward the place in me where, for a whole lifetime, I had accepted bad deals for myself from people around me. I had tried to please them, just because I was afraid to challenge them to the point where they would, I was sure, lash me with the truth about my gluttony or even slay me with the label *fat pig*. The relief made even that fear subside, and for the first time in my entire life, I knew that I was safe.

For the first time in my entire life, I knew that I was *safe*.

Can you imagine that? No wonder I use the word *home*. I wanted that meeting to go on for the rest of my life. I felt more peace and serenity during that hour and a half than in the previous four decades.

Obviously, I'm going again next week and will write about it. I am trying not to expect too much. The last thing I need now is another "silver bullet" that lets me down all over again. But I have to declare that this is something wonderful. In contrast with the high of the portrait, this feels more like a *center*, a solid place of balance and honesty.

January 25. Weight: 221½

I went back to Overeaters Anonymous this morning. It was mostly the same people I remember from last time, but some different faces too, I think.

Let me start with what is most important: I felt the same today as I felt last week. This place is home. These people are my family. We are related to each other in some terribly deep way I scarcely understand, but I am determined to understand it better before I'm through.

I began to get a little better sense of what this group is about today and to understand how the meeting works. I picked this up in two ways—first, by paying attention to what was happening; and second, from listening to a group member who took me aside during a break in the meeting to briefly describe how it works.

Overeaters Anonymous ("OA" to members) turns out to be a sister organization of Alcoholics Anonymous. They even use AA literature, just substituting a couple of words when they read it. When the AA literature says "alcohol," OA people say "food," and they substitute "compulsive overeater" for "alcoholic." All the rest stays the same. And it really makes sense, just as I suspected it would back when I was in contact with the alcoholism groups.

The whole thing is a volunteer deal, and a different person led the meeting today. They passed a basket for donations to help rent the room (most people put in a dollar), but otherwise it's strictly free. I guess this is what people call "self-help" groups, but I think "mutual help" is closer to what I see—and feel—happening.

That's what hit me all over again today: the deep bond of mutual caring and understanding. They—we—are all in the same boat, and for damned sure it isn't a boat any of us would have chosen. If misery loves company, these people have made an art of companionship.

But—and this is extremely important—they are not miserable. Far from it. I get the feeling they are all as eager to get into that room as I am, and that they really hunger for the understanding that flows among everyone. They talk about this "disease" of compulsive overeating and about their "recovery" from it. The sense I get is the opposite of misery; it is hope and determination and progress. You can feel it in the air. I inhaled it as deeply as I could today.

This morning I spoke what feels like the most important five words I have ever said out loud.

During the first part of the meeting, everyone was reading passages out of one of OA's regular books. One person would read a paragraph or two, then pass the book to the person next to them. Before reading, each of the people introduced him- or herself.

When my turn came, I said, "I am Eliot." Then I added those five words: "I am a compulsive overeater." The instant I spoke them, I was immediately overcome with emotion— just as I am right now, writing this. I began weeping, just as I am right now, writing this. Speaking those words—*I am a compulsive overeater*—meant everything to me. I was speaking a deep truth, a truth that lay at the very heart of my life and my pain. I was giving a name to my baffling disease, this enemy that has imprisoned me and tortured me and humiliated me for decades. And in naming it, I was beginning at last to meet it face to face. I was making public what I had struggled at such cost to hold private. I was making a connection between me and others after a lifetime of shamed isolation. I was declaring a problem.

And, most important of all, I was asking for help.

That may not sound like much, but it is nothing short of

earth-shattering for me. In many respects, it was the first time in my life I admitted there was something I couldn't handle.

Now I am struck by how hard it is for me to ask for help. I have spent my whole life believing I was supposed to be self-sufficient, equal to any challenge, capable of overcoming any obstacle, bright enough to learn anything, strong enough to master any shortcoming or weakness in myself. I grew up with powerful expectations laid on me. (My mother has been heard to declare on more than one occasion, "Of all my sons, I expect excellence; but of Eliot, I expect greatness." That is a difficult message for *all* her sons to live with, for lots of reasons.)

And so speaking those words—*I am a compulsive overeater*—felt like turning a real corner in my life somehow. I think I put myself into a different category of humanity today, like, "Welcome to the human race, superman. Join the crowd and let's see if we can help each other." I don't know where this is going to lead, but I am eager to find out.

As I reflect on the meeting, I realize I never heard a word of pride or self-satisfaction spoken. These OA people seem to thrive on their dependence on each other, and on their dependence on what they call a *Higher Power*. I don't know if this is a religious term or what. Maybe it just refers to the mutual support of the group itself. But whatever it is, everyone goes out of their way to insist that whatever ability they have to cope with their compulsive overeating, it comes from their dependence on a Power outside themselves. They are vigorous in denying their individual ability to deal with this disease one-on-one.

This is certainly the opposite of "willpower," and I don't understand it yet. But I'm sure I will, in time. Whatever it is these people know and have, I want some of it myself.

February 1. Weight: 220

I just got back from my third OA meeting. I am (if possible) even more gratified than ever. I experience these people as the most honest, caring, fearless group I have *ever* been with.

The honesty is what is so shocking. One of the people said this morning that, in her heart of hearts, she really felt she was superior to everyone else in the room. Everyone instantly *laughed!* What was clear from their general reaction (as well as my own: I laughed too) was that we *all* felt exactly the same. None of us wanted to be identified with a bunch of people trapped in a disease that nobody outside the room had any respect for.

But there was more to her honesty than that. The breathtaking part was her flat-out declaration of feeling superior, period. I felt like she was reading my mind—and clearly the others felt the same. I guess we all share something in our backgrounds that makes us look down on others to some degree. But what a thing to admit!

From what people in the room talk about and what the reading this morning stated, I would say that the group is more about humility and honesty than it is about food. That has to be the reason I experience such unbelievable relief when I am there—it is the one place where I don't have to lie to myself or to others about my eating behavior. I had no idea how much energy I put into keeping my insane behavior a secret, until I felt the way relief and freedom from fear lift me to unbelievably comfortable new realms of acceptance during those meetings.

The surprise, so far, is how little attention is paid to food. Nobody has talked about diets or calories or anything like that. No plans or charts, none of the stuff I am used to at Weight Watchers, Diet Center, et al. People talk about their *eating*, but not about food. (I gather there is even an agreement in the group not to mention particular foods by name.) A couple of people today were describing how powerfully they were tempted to overeat because of stresses—one had problems at work, the other was in the middle of a messy divorce—and how they had called other members of OA to get help in resisting the temptation to pig out.

I can't imagine myself doing that—calling somebody to say that I am on the verge of a binge: "Please stop me before I kill again!" That is just a little *too* humble for me, I think. I would hope I can handle those times by myself.

God! Listen to that! That is *just* the kind of thinking that has gotten me into this mess in the first place. And just the kind of thinking that the group has replaced with that beautiful, relief-giving atmosphere that fills the room. The atmosphere that says, "We *can't* do it by ourselves. If we could, we wouldn't be here. But since we can't, we'll help each other."

I am shocked at the power of the old, old message: Eliot should be able to do *anything* by himself.

Bullshit!

I just hope to God that I can erase that old message and let myself be open to the support of the group. It feels *so* good, all around me like a blanket—or a warm hug. But I am still a long way from being able to say anything myself, about where I am and what is bothering me. I am still very much a quiet observer at the meetings. I have a hard time imagining myself being as vulnerable there as some of the people I hear. But if that is what it takes, I'll find a way. What I have seen so far is much too precious to let slip away.

The things people share are startlingly honest. And the things don't necessarily have to do with a difficulty in coping with food temptations. One woman this morning broke down in tears as she recounted how she had lied under oath in court to protect her boss! She was scared to death, obviously, but when she finished telling us, there was a huge difference in her. She went from being a whimpering fifty-year-old child to someone who had actually recovered her dignity and self-respect, just in the act of speaking out loud what she had been struggling so hard to hide. You could see her making up her mind, declaring that from now on she was too valuable a person to sacrifice her honesty for her boss or anybody else who demanded that she corrupt herself as the price of "peace."

Amazingly, the group had no reaction whatsoever. Everybody just listened attentively (and very sympathetically). When she finished, she was hugged and comforted by the person next to her. Then, someone else began sharing what he had written on a different subject entirely.

Apparently, another custom of the group is that no one, ever, talks directly to another person as an individual. Nobody ever comments, directly or indirectly, on what someone else has just shared or gives them advice. The group simply functions as a totally accepting, understanding hearer of struggles and "confessions." There is not a trace of judgment or contempt.

Nobody that I could see even seemed surprised as she told her tale. It was like they were all thinking, *Why, sure. I understand how you could have done that. I probably would have done the same myself, in the same situation.* Such humility all around the room, nothing but nods of understanding. That must be why the group feels safe to me.

February 8. Weight: 220

I am falling into a rhythm of writing just once a week now, when I return from the Saturday morning OA meeting. That seems to be a good arrangement. My constant business travels jerk me around too much during the week to find a block of time when I can really feel and think my way into what is happening on this front, and the meetings provide me with plenty of food for thought.

Which brings me to today's meeting. In preparation for the meeting, I read some pamphlets I picked up last week and Step One in the book *Twelve Steps and Twelve Traditions*. What I read has made me take this experience very seriously.

First, it is clear that OA regards compulsive overeating as a disease. More than a disease, it is considered a progressive, *fatal* disease. At first, that struck me as a bit melodramatic. I know cancer is a fatal disease, and I can even see that alcoholism is a fatal disease in the sense that people die from the complications of alcoholism, such as kidney failure. But how could *eating* be a fatal disease?

I am embarrassed at how blind I am. What the hell else am *I* doing but dying? Sure, some powerhouse beta-blockers are supposedly holding off my first heart attack and may prevent the stroke that would turn me into a household pet for my wife and children to feed and bathe. But for how long? Give me a few more years of uncontrolled overeating and I can surely defeat even the best efforts of medical science to keep me alive. I am doing a ponderous dance of slow-motion suicide. That's all there is to it.

If my compulsive overeating is what is making me do it, then it is a fatal disease beyond any doubt.

So I am taking a more sober look at this and trying to figure out how OA can help me. As I mentioned before, it seems to be a program of Twelve Steps, and they talk of "working the Steps." The Step we covered today—Step One—sure goes to the heart of it. It says: "We admitted we were powerless over food and that our lives had become unmanageable."

On the one hand, that says it all. I know beyond a shadow of doubt that I really am powerless over food; this "experiment" has proved that conclusively. And my eating, as a result, is unmanageable.

On the other hand, what came clear in the discussion today, and in my own reactions, was how much more is involved here. For starters, the very notion of being "powerless" sticks in the craw of any red-blooded American man (or woman, I would imagine) who has been raised to believe they are destined for greatness. My pride is on the line here. Well, O.K., I can admit, I do have this little problem with food. So I'm powerless over food. But that's it, right?

Wrong. When people at the meeting talked about this Step, they weren't just talking about their eating being unmanageable because of this disease. The Step says "our *lives* had become unmanageable." I am beginning to see what the people at the meeting mean. Person after person shared incidents in which they were failing to handle situations, or were ducking responsibilities, or were bending over backwards too far in order to please other people—all because of their obsession with food and their instinct to run away and bury themselves in a binge.

I have to say it all rings true. Too true. I know I head for the kitchen as a knee-jerk reaction to stress, as a way to avoid handling some sticky situation, or when I just don't know what to do. When in doubt, stuff your face and hope the problem will go away. I never realized before this morning's discussion how usual a reaction that is for me, how typically and relentlessly I turn to food when I am feeling unsure.

I do have one major advantage for the moment, anyhow. I *know* I am powerless over food and need help with it. I don't think I could get myself to take part in these meetings if I didn't know that. I'd still be looking in vain for the next magic trick, for the latest in Eliot's lifelong string of failed exercises in self-reliance and "willpower." The greatest blessing of this OA connection so far is that it gives me permission to relinquish the hopeless fantasy of being able to do it on my own and the permission to ask for help. Even that much feels like the beginning of a miracle.

The heart of this budding miracle is the lifting of my *shame.* I was suffocating in self-hatred before. There was no end to my contempt for my weakness, my guilt, my shame at not being able to control my eating. And my fat body shouts my weakness for all the world to hear, making my shame a never-ending agony. Every time I passed a store window and stole a look at myself, every time I was forced to purchase clothing, every time I ordered from a menu, every time almost anything happened that called attention to my body, the alarm went off in me: *you are a worthless slob.*

I have not felt those feelings *once* since I walked into that first OA meeting.

Do you know what a miracle is? I have just described one. No word short of *miracle* is powerful enough to describe the lifting of that self-hatred I stewed in every single day of my life.

The lifting of that contempt is a gift that comes from being part of the OA meeting, and obviously is not a result of any weight loss. (I haven't lost any weight—yet.) I have the feeling that no matter what happens, no matter how long I stay in OA, no matter if I ever lose this fat I so detest, the understanding and acceptance of my problem by my fellow OA members will banish that shame forever. I know that I am all right in their eyes, cared for not because I am perfect but precisely because I am not.

How can I grasp what a revolution this is for me? Feeling

loved because of my *weakness*, instead of believing I have to be perfect in order to be worthwhile, worth loving? No wonder I want to use the word *miracle*.

I am beginning to feel like these OA people and I are in this thing together for the long haul.

February 15. Weight: 220

I think it's time to get down to work. So, during this morning's meeting, I made a list of the things I would do if I were really serious about being part of OA. Here's my list:

1. Find a food sponsor.
2. Find a Step sponsor.
3. Develop a food plan.
4. Buy a notebook.
5. Read the OA literature.
6. Make a phone call.

About sponsors. Because OA is all about people helping each other, everybody has a sponsor—or two. Sponsors are veterans of the program who teach newcomers like me the ropes.

A *food sponsor* is someone who helps you plan what you are going to eat *and* who sort of looks over your shoulder every day to help you stick to it. A *Step sponsor* helps you work the Steps, doing whatever the program suggests as the way to deal with this disease.

The way most people get sponsors is to pick out someone at the meeting and ask her or him. This makes sense, since after a few weeks I already have a pretty good feel for which people I can relate to best. But there is a problem. Most of them are already sponsoring someone, and only a couple are available. And the available ones are women. That is no problem for me, but OA encourages same-gender sponsoring and I can understand that. The depth of emotional bonding between people in the room is very powerful during meetings, and it takes no great imagination to envision that entanglements could result from daily contact between sponsors and newcomers talking one to one, even though most of it is done over the phone. Since there are very few men in my group, I'll have to look elsewhere in the organization. (There are other OA meetings in the area—one every night of the week, in fact.)

At the meeting this morning, they circulated a flier announcing an all-day OA meeting coming up in a couple of weeks. Apparently, they do these "marathon" meetings every once in a while. The flyer listed several names and phone numbers as contact people. One of them is a man—Andrew. I'm going to call him and see if he'll be my sponsor. I am serious about getting into this thing, and I figure anybody who is organizing a day-long meeting has to be pretty serious about it himself.

I thought I would feel funny hooking up with a sponsor, but somehow I don't. I haven't felt like an apprentice for a long, long time. In fact, I have spent a lot of energy trying to convince myself and others what an expert I am at everything. (And look where it has gotten me!)

I'll call Andrew when I finish writing.

The food plan is next on my list. Everybody has a food plan they work out with their food sponsor. They write down exactly what they will eat on any given day, when they will eat it, and—most importantly—precisely how much of each food they will eat. Many of these people believe it is important to weigh and measure everything they plan to eat.

I understand that, for sure. Ask me to estimate a "reasonable" portion of something I have a craving for, whether lasagna or ice cream or chocolate chip cookies, and I'm likely to put a pound or more of it on a plate. For my first helping.

My getting-serious list also includes a notebook. It's for taking to meetings to jot down interesting things other people say and to write my response to the question of the day.

The literature, next on the list, I have already gotten; I just need to read more of it more often.

But the phone call, the final item. That feels like a hurdle of sorts.

OA people call each other on the phone between meetings. I never have, and I haven't been called yet either; but I know it goes on and forms a strong part of the program because they follow a process at each meeting for exchanging phone numbers.

I feel a little stupid about calling somebody. What do I say? "Hi, this is Eliot from the OA meetings. Hope you're having a nice day?" I guess that's exactly what some do. Others—and I can understand this better—call somebody when they feel on the verge of attacking the refrigerator for a binge. I don't know whether I have the guts—or humility—to do that, but I can understand it.

Maybe humility is the hurdle. Making a call seems like a test to me. I think it means swallowing my pride. Can I imagine myself calling someone just because I *need* them, because I need the connection with them? Yuk! That is *not* my style.

But if my style were all I think it's cracked up to be, I wouldn't weigh 220 pounds and spend my business days shuffling around in a decidedly unstylish one-suit wardrobe. (I was forced to go buy a giant-sized suit to fit my fatter-than-ever body so I'd have *some*thing to wear. But I was damned if

I'd buy more than one, since that would mean I was planning to stay that fat.) So I know I have to get up my courage and make a call to one of these people some day, for no reason other than to knuckle under to a different way of behaving. Well, I'll start with calling this Andrew and find out how that goes first.

February 16. Weight: 220

I couldn't wait until next Saturday to write again. I reached Andrew on the phone this morning and I think I struck gold! My instinct to call someone who is really serious seems to have been dead-on. He has been in OA for nine years; during the first two years, he lost one hundred pounds and—more importantly—has kept every pound of it off in the seven years since! There may be hope for me yet!

What's more, he said he would be delighted to be both my food sponsor *and* my step sponsor. Two for the price of one. He seemed to think it was just as easy to combine the two roles, and I feel a lot of relief. I wasn't looking forward to having to scout around for two different guys, since men are a distinct minority in the program. Andrew suggested I meet him at the marathon meeting on the 23rd so we can discuss how to get started.

I am suddenly feeling drained. I know part of it is relief, getting this awkward request out of the way. But there is more to it. I think I am feeling something more like dependence. That's pretty close to it. I have just turned to some guy I never met before in my life and asked him to help me, please. Me, the guy who always wants to be seen as all-knowing, self-sufficient, in charge. Asking some stranger to take care of me. And what I am feeling is *good* about it. Can this be the beginnings of humility?

God knows it's far preferable to humiliation. I've been thinking about the difference between humility and humiliation. I

always thought that asking for help was the ultimate humiliation, the final declaration of my stupidity and unworthi-
ness. But I have just survived that experience and feel better
than I have in years. I somehow feel more *real*, less a phony,
less out on a limb, less the great imposter. I feel like I
have lowered a heavy mask and am standing here uncov-
ered, waiting for what is next—and not fearing whatever
comes next.

Now I realize this is more an experience of humility than
humiliation.

Humiliation better describes the relationship between me and
food. Humiliation is standing in front of the kitchen counter
listening to the sixth bagel in the bag order me to cram it into
my mouth and chew it with jaws already tired from mashing
the previous five. Or digging through the garbage can, for
God's sake, to find the Styrofoam tray the Sara Lee cake
came on so I can scrape the last remains of frosting and
crumbs. Or trying to cover up my sneak-eating by rearrang-
ing the cookies on a tray—or even shaking up the nuts in a
jar, to redistribute them—to make it look like none had been
taken and stuffed into Eliot's already painfully swollen belly.
Or being caught out in the kitchen polishing off a plate of
food I had offered, so helpfully, to clear from the table—
knowing all the time my sole objective was to be alone with
that food and attack it.

That is humiliation.

I think I'll settle for humility any day.

February 22. Weight: 218

I had two firsts today. Today was the first time that I spoke
up in the meeting and the first time I made a spontaneous
phone call to another member. I just decided it was time. I

began to fear that, if I didn't, I was going to miss out somehow, on something—I'm not sure what. Let me grope my way into this.

Holding back. I have been holding back, somehow. Sure, I say (and mean) the words "I am a compulsive overeater," and I *love* the freedom and integrity I feel when I do. But I haven't yet quite acted, in the group, as though I also believed that meant I had a fatal disease from which I could be rescued only by people or powers beyond myself. That's it. I've somehow acted (and thought, probably) that I could just sit back and learn what I needed and then take it and self-sufficiently apply it all by my lonesome, just like I always have.

Well, I broke through that today. I finally spoke up in the meeting. All I said was something like, "I am speaking up because I have to. I know there is a barrier of resistance in me to do this, and the only reason I am talking is to break that barrier. Thank you." But it was a hurdle for me, and I know it puts me further into this process.

I confirmed that I had broken the barrier—for today, anyhow—by calling one of the guys in the group later in the day.

He couldn't have been more gracious—or more grateful for the call, he said. He had been struggling with some food temptation this very afternoon—a surprise to me, since he is really slender. My call came at just the right time to break him out of the inner battle he was having about whether to ignore his food plan for the day and indulge in a "small binge."

He described himself as being in a "white knuckle" condition, and I really understood what that meant. It is so tough to resist when those cravings hit and the voice of temptation (he called it "the disease talking") is so smooth and ever so reasonable. *Just a little now. Then you can skip something else later.* How many times I have heard and obeyed. Going one-on-one with that voice is surefire disaster. As somebody at the meeting put it last week, "Whenever I get inside my own head, I know I am behind enemy lines." That's why OA people really push the use of the phone between meetings— to break that isolation. And I know the guy I called meant it when he said my call was "inspired." I feel pretty good about that.

February 23. Weight: 218

Today, I had my scheduled meeting with Andrew, my sponsor-to-be. I don't know what I expected, but it sure wasn't the guy I met: late thirties, balding, bearded, relatively short, and built more like a jockey than a hefty eater. Really, he can't weigh more than about 140 or so—trim and compact. (I think my skepticism must have showed somehow because, while we were talking, he pulled out a picture of himself at about 240. What a sight! His face looked like a balloon about to pop—eyes just slits, cheeks as wide as his ears, chin that melted into his chest. Anyone could see that inside this blimp was a very unhappy man.)

We didn't have a lot of time, since he had to emcee the meeting in a few minutes, so we got right down to business. He told me that we needed to work out a food plan together— what I would be eating, as a regular pattern—and that I was to call him every day (we agreed on 6:30 P.M. as mutually convenient) to tell him what I would be eating for the next three meals. This is called "committing" your food.

Every day? Every single day? At first, this seemed like carrying things just a bit far, but I am resolved to follow where this program leads and not try to second-guess it along the way.

If these mostly trim and almost universally relaxed, congenial people got the way they are by following these Steps, well, I want some of what they have and I'll do whatever I have to.

But I'm getting ahead of myself. I want to record more about the meetings at the "marathon." The leader in the first meeting I went to began by telling us the story of her life as a compulsive overeater. (In OA terminology, this personal story-telling is called *qualifying*. The person qualifying speaks of his or her experience before and after joining OA and of how OA helps them.) Well, her story was absolutely gripping! What made it gripping was how much it was like my own experiences—and those of everyone else, judging from the constant nods of recognition and the occasional unconscious "uh-huh" when she described her sneak-eating, her humiliation, her fears of being found out, her hatred of clothes-shopping, and all the rest.

Well, it wasn't all "before" stuff. She went on to describe how, after repeated failures of diet after diet and many of the same kind of willpower calisthenics I have tried, she finally gave up all pretense of being able to handle it herself and waddled into an OA meeting. She then went on to talk about what the experience has meant to her and what she has gained from it.

She talked a lot about changes in her life as a result of being in the OA program. She has lost ninety pounds and has kept to her food plan for three years now. (Eating nothing but what is on your food plan is called being *abstinent*— considered very, very important.) But this woman clearly felt—and said—that losing weight was the *least* significant of the changes she has experienced. (I have been hearing this a lot, in bits and snatches, at the Saturday meeting, and it is clear that this program is life-changing in more ways than one. Come to think of it, I guess that is what I am sensing when I described OA people earlier as "almost universally relaxed." They really are the most open, nondefensive, nonthreatening people I have *ever* met.) She went on to describe how some of her relationships had gotten so much better since she abandoned her lifelong game plan of managing everyone else's life for them.

That really struck home. I am starting to recognize the degree to which I have adopted the role of General Manager of the Universe, feeling responsible for controlling the outcome of every situation and every one else's decisions. The list makes me cringe even as it begins to form itself in my head right now: the way I have biased the choices in remodelling our house by keeping the full range of options hidden from my wife; the way I "helpfully" presented my kids with manipulated introductions to people and predigested alternatives for how they might spend their summers; the way I sold my wife's car—which she dearly loved—over her protests, on the grounds that it was unsafe, so I could unload my car on her and buy the car *I* really wanted. It hurts too much to add to the list. But I know I could, and will.

Time to call Andrew to "commit" my food; I think I'll resume writing later.

Back now, and what an experience! What happened? Nothing, and everything. The *nothing* was that I dialed Andrew's number, he answered, I read to him what I had written as the plan for my next three meals, he said O.K., and I got off the phone.

Now, about the *everything*. For the first time in my life, the food that I am going to eat is an open, respectable, truthful, legitimate, acceptable, shame-free matter of fact. Fact. Just pure fact. "For breakfast, I am going to eat a container of plain yogurt sweetened with Equal, one navel orange, and an English muffin. For lunch . . . For dinner . . ."

What does this mean? It means for the first time that I *know* that this is exactly what I *am* going to eat, that it is *all* I am going to eat, and that I have made a contract with another person to whom I have *committed* myself.

This is *so* far from a lifetime of trying to keep everyone in the world from knowing what I am eating, of trying to avoid making any commitments to myself or anyone else so I will have plenty of leeway to add on, to bust out, to rearrange, to substitute, to cheat, to binge, to kill myself some more.

With one phone call, that is all over. With that one phone call, I am somehow, suddenly, bound to someone who knows how deeply I want to eat more than that, who will support my determination to eat *only* what I committed, and who will give his blessing to what I actually do eat. It's like I have *permission* to eat what I committed and feel good about it. It's like I have a *right* to eat what I committed.

This is really important: *I have never before felt a right to eat what I was eating,* because I knew in my shame-filled heart of hearts that I was eating so much else on the sly that I shouldn't be eating. I felt I had no real right to eat anything at all.

That just came to a halt with my phone call to Andrew. Suddenly, I want to commit everything I am going to eat every day for the rest of my life, just to keep feeling the relief I feel right now, the clean rush of pure honesty that is sweeping through me.

I am reminded of something I heard someone say at an OA meeting: "Nothing tastes as good as abstinence feels." I think I really understand that.

February 25. Weight: 217

Looks like this will be the last time I start an entry with my weight. Andrew, my sponsor, told me to stop weighing myself every day; once a month, he said, is plenty.

We talked about the reasoning behind it and it sure makes sense. I have lived and died by the numbers on the scale, and usually they worked against me. When the numbers on the scale went up, I felt terrible—and usually went downstairs and promptly stuffed my face with some food to blot out the lousy feelings the scale inflicted. The net effect was the same if the numbers showed I had lost weight—but for a different reason. If I had lost a pound or two, I felt I could "reward" myself with something extra. Either way, the scale sent me toward the food.

And stupid as it feels to confess, I must say I have given the scale a lot of power. I gave it the power to make me feel good or bad, to send me to the refrigerator in despair or glee, to make me act like an idiot. I wonder how many days I have weighed myself two or three times, just out of obsessive concern for my relative fatness that day.

I mean, how idiotic is it to be so frantic about what judgment the scale will render that I will not only go to the bathroom before I weigh but—God, this is so ridiculous!—actually debate whether to shower before or after weighing. Why? Simple: I know that my body and hair will absorb water, which weighs something, and some of that water will remain even after I towel off. I certainly don't want that water to distort my true weight now, do I? After all, it might add, what, all of one or two ounces to my 220 or so pounds! Why, heavens, I couldn't bear the injustice of it all!

Isn't that insane? I really begin to see why OA calls this a *disease*. Anything that has the capacity to make an otherwise reasonably sane adult go through such mental gyrations deserves the label *disease;* it sure doesn't have anything to do with health, I know that much.

We also spent some time talking about abstinence. Abstinence from alcohol is easy to define: none. Just never let alcohol pass your lips. Period.

Not so easy when it comes to food. "Abstinence" is a quirky term when applied to eating. Obviously, the alcoholics' standard—no, not ever, never—won't work when it comes to eating.

But for people who are seeking control of what has been uncontrolled, and limits to what has been limitless, we have to draw some lines. After a lifetime in which too much was never enough, how do you determine what is just right for you?

Trying to set the boundaries between "just right" and "too much" is tough. I have to face that stuff every day, and I have long since learned how food can call out to me and make me come eat it. A plate of freshly baked chocolate chip cookies destroys my judgment. The aroma, the first bite, the relief from whatever I was worrying about—they all flood over me and make me forget about limits. How many have I had? Six? Nine? Oh, fifteen? Well, maybe just one or two more, then I really *must* stop.

It's just as bad at the table. Seconds? Why, yes, it was delicious. I'd *love* just a tad more, thanks. (More often, I would conspire to spoon out the seconds myself, to make sure I got "enough.")

Clearly, I need some guidelines. But OA as an organization does not offer or suggest any diets or food plans. (I guess that figures. Heaven knows the world is full of perfectly sensible food plans; if that is all it took, I would have been trim ever since the day I went on my first diet as a teenager.) It seems like that's where the sponsor comes in.

Andrew says the boundaries of my abstinence are to be defined by weighing and measuring all my food. He says there is no more critical step in maintaining my abstinence than this. I have no difficulty understanding the reasoning behind it: I can be totally dishonest with myself about how much I am eating. I know all too well how this disease of compulsive overeating makes me a liar to myself, or shouts down the feeble voice of sanity in me that tries to set mental limits on how much I will eat.

But four ounces is four ounces. And one cup is one cup. Period. No debate. No scheming. So if my lunch is four ounces of turkey and two ounces of wheat bread and one cup of strawberries, that's it. And if some little voice in me says I can skip weighing and measuring today—*after all, you're a pretty good judge of the size of these quantities by now, aren't you?*—then I guess I'd know whose voice that is.

The thought of having those boundaries brings another wave of relief to me. Suddenly there is no debate. Another miracle. No more energy being endlessly drained into that secret wrestling match, no more churning of the guilt and the shame, no more wondering if I will emerge from a meal hating myself once again. No more playing games about having this little extra now and having a little less at the next feeding. If I can keep all this open and aboveboard with Andrew, that will all be over now.

God, I hope I have the guts to stay honest about this. It is my only chance.

So Andrew and I spent considerable time working out the exact amounts of food I would eat on my food plan, as well as what kinds of foods were "in" and "out." Certain things are absolutely, positively out: sugar, alcohol, bleached flour.

I am ready to be rid of sugar. I know beyond any doubt that it is a physically addictive substance for me. I have learned that through previous diets when I abstained from sugar. I could feel a deep chemical change in my body, and many of my cravings went away. But as soon as I resumed eating foods with high sugar content, the cravings returned like a tidal wave, and I was swept helplessly before them.

Alcohol is harder to give up entirely. I am not an alcoholic, after all, I am a compulsive overeater.

But I also know, from sad experience, that alcohol has as powerful an effect on my craving to eat as sugar does. When I get home after a long evening with wine, I go nuts trying to get at something chocolate or, failing that, almost anything intensely sweet: an English muffin (or three or four) piled with jam, a quart of ice cream, leftover candies from trick-or-treating.

When I laid off alcohol on previous diets, it clearly helped. And I know it hurt my cause when I inevitably reintroduced alcohol into my system. Within days, I would be back into heavily sugared foods.

So I guess I am ready to declare alcohol off limits. Besides, the OA program and Andrew keep repeating that we are not doing this for a lifetime—only for today. "One day at a time" is a motto I hear a lot at meetings.

As for bleached flour, that is a different matter. When Andrew suggested outlawing it, I asked why. After all, it is a staple of baked goods, and I will be having some baked goods (two ounces per meal) on my food plan. So why no bleached flour? "Because you need the discipline," came the answer. I was certainly in no position to argue, and for the future (one day at a time) I will go to the extra trouble of locating baked goods made with unbleached flour.

I'm beginning to get handles on what this abstinence is all about. It seems like it has the effect of taking food down from the pedestal, where I have worshipped it all these years, and converting it into a routine utility. All the sex appeal of food is stripped away, and it becomes an almost mechanical process: one ounce of this, two ounces of that, a half cup of something else. Then get on with the rest of your affairs.

Two things that I hear at meetings are starting to sum it up for me:

• Nothing tastes as good as abstinence feels.
• Three meals a day and life in between.

Three meals a day and life in between! It's the "life in between" that I am beginning to see as something new; my continuing obsession with food has obscured a lot of my life. All the hours I spent fantasizing about my next meal or stuffing my face between meals was time I was *not* living my life; I was avoiding my life.

I am a great avoider. I am coming to see that. I avoid conflict. I avoid sticky situations. I avoid being strong or strict or exposed or vulnerable. And I guess I have run for the kitchen every time I felt a tingle of danger arise, every time I felt I might be drawn into a situation where I would be inadequate, feel inadequate, or be perceived as inadequate.

Why the hell should I have to be so "adequate" all the time? Maybe if I can recognize that I am so genuinely inadequate in matters about food, I can also recognize my inadequacy in other things—and that it is O.K.! After all, I *know* it is O.K. to have this disease of compulsive overeating. In fact, I *love* knowing I have it. It explains so much of my life, so much of my confusion, so much of my despair. God! The relief that comes with admitting—declaring—my compulsive overeating is so deep, so total. Maybe I can begin to experience that same kind of relief in other areas of my life by admitting—declaring—my inadequacies there too.

Suddenly, I am overwhelmed with how sick and tired I am of trying to be perfect. I am exhausted and defeated by my life-long efforts to cover up any ignorance or any shortcomings. Why should I have to be perfect, anyhow? Who the hell ever said it wasn't O.K. for me not to know some things, not to be competent in some areas, not to care about other things. I don't have to be good at *everything*, do I?

I was made aware at an OA meeting of how much I expect of myself. Several people were sharing stories of their perfectionism, of how they were driven to do everything just right every time. I volunteered that I guessed I was no perfectionist, because I don't think I ever do *anything* well enough. The others immediately laughed in a good-natured way that puzzled me for a moment. Then, I realized with a smile that *only* a perfectionist could say what I had. A nonperfectionist would have been more than satisfied with all the things I thought I was doing poorly.

Once I accepted the truth of that observation, suddenly a whole pattern of my perfectionism came into focus. Did we need a new toaster? I would have consulted consumer reports in the library, visited five or six stores, and examined fifteen or twenty different models before settling—warily—on the one I decided was the very best. All this for a purchase that cost less than tickets for a spur-of-the-moment movie.

Crazier yet, I would choose to do nothing, or to go without something entirely (depriving my family, too, of course) if I couldn't do it perfectly or couldn't afford the very best. Thus, we went for years—and I mean years and *years*—with no outdoor furniture whatsoever to enjoy on our large covered porch overlooking a nice yard, because I had it in mind that only antique wicker would satisfy my vision of what should be there. We might as well have lived in the subway for all the enjoyment we got out of our porch and yard, thanks to my perfectionistic image of what would be fitting for me and mine.

I feel as though this OA program may be Eliot's "Great Awakening"!

March 1

I have now completed a full week of abstinence, and it feels marvelous. I have no idea whether the abstinence has led to weight loss—and I almost don't even care! I know that sounds silly after so many years of frantic diets and after so much concern that my current weight is killing me.

Whether I lose weight or not, there is something I have already gained by being abstinent—the right to say "I'm hungry." Sound strange?

Before I became abstinent, I would go to any lengths to avoid calling attention to anything related to eating, including my own legitimate need to eat. Fearing a possible remark about my already being too well fed, I would be the last to ever acknowledge any desire to eat: "Hey, no problem, whenever everybody else is ready."

One of the most startling and welcome gifts of abstinence, then, was feeling the right to say for the first time in my life, guilt-free, "I am hungry and I need to eat now."

But something else has emerged as even more important. What has taken over is a kind of sobriety, a quiet, day-by-day lowering of my anxiety level about food. It feels almost under control. Not under *my* control. But under the control of this OA program. My nightly call to Andrew, for example, is the real cornerstone of my life right now. I find myself eager to check in with him, to depend on his being there to hear my food plan and to confirm to me that everything is O.K. with my food. During this past week, my business travels have taken me across the country, but I made it a point to put in my call to Andrew at precisely 6:30. On one day, that meant excusing myself from a business meeting in California at 3:30 in the afternoon to reach Andrew at 6:30 in New Jersey. But I didn't feel the least bit hesitant about doing that; there is a rising tide of assertiveness in me about taking care of first things first—and this program for my compulsive overeating is definitely first. If it isn't, I'm a dead man, sooner or later.

The beauty of my current condition is that I know, beyond a shadow of a doubt, that I need help. I know that I am powerless over food, that food has humiliated and savaged me relentlessly throughout my whole shame-drenched life. I know I cannot cope with it by myself, and I know that people like Andrew can provide me with the structure and support I must have if I am to survive this disease and die of something more sensible, a lot later on.

This is really a change for me. I have been in the program only a matter of weeks, but I genuinely feel serene—*serene* is the right word—about needing this help. That is such a new feeling for me—to acknowledge that I need help and to feel O.K. about acknowledging it. This is definitely something new growing in me. I just hope to God that I can hang onto it.

What a relief to be free from obsession with food! I used to think about food *all* the time. Not with my whole mind, of course, since I needed some of it to do my work and relate to the people around me. But part of my mind was always thinking of food: thinking about what I would have for my next meal; calculating how soon I could reach for the next chip and dip without triggering the thought in anyone's mind that Eliot is really pigging out on the hors d'oeuvres; or deciding whether I should clear the table so I could snatch a few extra mouthfuls while alone in the kitchen. At business lunches or cocktail parties, some portion of my thinking and attention was constantly on the food—*will anybody else want to order dessert?*—and not on the people and issues and tasks at hand. My obsession with food crippled my ability to function every day at full power.

That obsession has just plain been lifted from me. I don't know where it went, but it is gone. Oh, I do have an occasional thought about the next meal, but it's different from before.

I am certainly not preoccupied as I once was by constant schemes to get more food, and most days I give only routine thought to planning and shopping for my meals.

On a couple of occasions, though, when it began to feel that I was spending time scheming again, I took that as a danger signal: it is my disease speaking to me, tempting me to pay more attention to food than to my program of recovery.

And so I have decided that when I find that "food is talking to me," I know what to do: pick up the phone and call my sponsor or another OA member. I did it the other day and it is so easy, and so effective. This is a disease of isolation, and when I am alone and isolated with thoughts of food, I am a goner. I know where that one leads—I have almost fifty years of pain to remind me. When I go one-on-one with food, I am going to lose every time.

So I hope I can find the humility to make that kind of call whenever food starts calling me. All it takes is for me to abandon the notion that I "should" be able to handle it by myself. Every time that thought crops up, I know it is my disease speaking—appealing to my pride, telling me all over again that if I just had enough willpower, I could get through this little temptation by myself. *What's the matter, Eliot, can't handle it?*

No, I can't. And I am learning to resist the temptation to prove I can.

So far I feel pretty determined. I made that first "I need help" call. And I am really assertive with my family, friends, and business associates about putting my OA program needs first. I have caused some reshuffling of others' calendars to accommodate my meetings and phone calls, but that's all right. I *need* this and I am going to get this. I don't have a choice. Fortunately, they all seem to understand and support me.

March 5

I went to the Wednesday OA meeting last night to see what it was like. I learned a lot. Unlike the read-a-chapter-and-write-about-it format of Saturday, this was more like the individual sessions at the marathon, where the leader "qualifies"—tells a roomful of fellow members the truth about his or her life as a compulsive overeater.

But before that, there were a number of readings that I found extremely helpful.

For starters, they began by reading something called "The Promises," a wonderfully appealing prospect:

> If we are painstaking about this phase of our development, we will be amazed before we are half way through. We are going to know a new freedom and a new happiness. We will not regret the past nor wish to shut the door on it. We will comprehend the word serenity and we will know peace. No matter how far down the scale we have gone, we will see how our experience can benefit others. That feeling of uselessness and self-pity will disappear. We will lose interest

in selfish things and gain interest in our fellows. Self-seeking will slip away. Our whole attitude and outlook upon life will change. Fear of people and of economic insecurity will leave us. We will intuitively know how to handle situations which used to baffle us. We will suddenly realize that God is doing for us what we could not do for ourselves.*

All that sounds so wondrous and idealistic that I would be highly skeptical of it—would treat it like one of those ads for How to Make a Million in Real Estate with No Money Down—were it not for what I feel and observe.

What I feel is the beginning of those promises coming true for me. Already I am more relaxed than I have ever been in my life, just by abandoning so much of my hopeless effort to control the world—or even to control my compulsive over-eating. I am leaning on others and accepting my weakness. And I feel so much stronger for having done so.

Already, I feel able to handle awkward situations that used to baffle me—situations where others put inappropriate demands on me; situations where I wanted to run away; situations where food was calling to me and I was under its spell.

I feel without a doubt that God is involved in this somehow. I'm not sure how yet, but I expect I'll find out in due course.

As for what I observe, these OA people are truly *different*. I don't know what they are like at home or at work, but at the meetings, they are the most honest, caring, sensitive, courageous, unselfish people I have ever met, anywhere. They are almost too good to be true.

And when they "qualify" or simply share informally during the meeting, they actually reflect The Promises. Person after

---

Alcoholics Anonymous, 3rd ed. (New York: A.A. World Services, Inc., 1976), 83-84. Reprinted by permission of A.A. World Services, Inc.

person describes situations where they are experiencing or living out the kind of life The Promises describe.

Following the reading of The Promises, we read some material about "The Tools of Recovery." These include abstinence, sponsorship, and meetings, all of which I feel comfortably familiar with by now. The material went on to describe the use of the telephone, for example, as a "tool," and I found that helpful. I have only made a couple of calls other than my nightly call to my sponsor, and I still feel a little hesitant about it.

But the readings reminded me that compulsive overeating is a disease of isolation. We hide out, ashamed and alone. We do our best to handle it on our own. We keep trying a failed strategy, to take on the disease one-on-one, even though we have a lifetime of failure as evidence that our go-it-alone approach will *never* work. Making a call is a simple way to declare surrender, to escape the insanity of repeating certain failure, and to relax into the network of support that other members offer.

I know that I have felt very good on the few occasions when someone from OA has called me in recent weeks; I guess it's time to start reciprocating.

Curiously, the readings also mentioned anonymity as one of the tools. I suppose it is a tool, since we use it faithfully. There is a wonderful freedom that comes with being able to say anything—really *anything*—in those meetings, without any fear of repercussion. I have heard people unburden themselves of a gut-wrenching and mind-blowing array of personal concerns in those meetings. They could do it only because it is so utterly *safe* there. I am sure the anonymity plays a big part in creating that climate of safety.

Another tool is the OA literature, which is available at meetings. In addition to the two basic books of the program,

Twelve Steps and Twelve Traditions and *Alcoholics Anonymous* (also referred to as "The Big Book"), I have picked up several pamphlets that help explain the way to work the Steps and things like that. (I am learning that OA is a free-form outfit, and the way anybody does anything is pretty much up to how a sponsor and newcomer work it out between them.)

I said sponsor and "newcomer," but I have come to realize that almost everybody has a sponsor—even those who have been in for ten years and are themselves sponsoring two or three people at a time. This is clearly a basic belief: you don't *ever* "recover" from this disease and get on top of it to the point where you can handle it yourself.

That's an idea that takes some getting used to. On one hand, I certainly can't imagine myself going to weekly meetings ten or twenty years from now. On the other hand, the ruling motto is "one day at a time." So far, I cherish the effect and would do anything to keep it going. If calling my sponsor every day and going to a meeting once a week is what it takes, I'll keep doing it as long as it keeps working. I know damned well what awaits me when and if it ever stops working.

March 26

Today is a triple celebration: I have completed one whole month of abstinence. I weighed myself today and have lost nine pounds in the past month. And I am going to begin my "Step work" in the OA program.

Let's begin with the month of abstinence. I am not sure whether I have ever kept to a "diet" without cheating for a whole month before—probably not—but even if I have, there is no comparison whatsoever. This abstinence business is something very different from a diet. A diet is what you wait to get *off*.

Abstinence is what you strive to keep up—forever, one day at a time. There couldn't be a more profound difference.

And I increasingly take to heart each day that line I heard at one of those first meetings: Nothing tastes as good as abstinence feels.

Andrew has given me some reading to do, starting with the chapter on Step One in *Twelve Steps and Twelve Traditions* ("Twelve and Twelve" in OA jargon). The First Step is one I find easy to grasp. It says, simply: "We admitted we were powerless over food—that our lives had become unmanageable."

I can say those words with absolutely no fear of contradiction. If ever there was a guy who has proved to himself beyond a shadow of a doubt that he was powerless over food, I am he. OA people talk of the need to "surrender" to the disease in order to ask for the help one needs. I have declared unconditional surrender, flown the white flag, laid down my willpower and whatever other weapons I fumbled around with, and come on bended knee.

Andrew has assigned me some writing (which I will read to him at a later date) about reaching this point.

He also asked me to write about how my life had become unmanageable as a result of my compulsive overeating, and that takes a bit more thinking.

For starters, I began thinking about my procrastination. I used to regard it as a natural way to be, simply my own pace of doing things. There was almost nothing that I couldn't put off until tomorrow—or the next day.

I am beginning to realize it has been linked to my compulsive overeating. I know I have used food as a tranquilizer, as an escape hatch to jump down whenever I confronted something I wasn't sure I could handle.

This really takes on ridiculous proportions in my life. I leave relatively simple matters untended for months and sometimes years.

A case in point: I "helped" my son buy a van for his summer house-painting business. He didn't need or ask for my help; I'm a great one, however, for considering that a minor impediment easily overcome by aggressive fatherly concern.

The five-year-old van turned out to be a turkey. My son was barely able to coax it, sputtering and stalling, the twenty miles from the dealership to our place. It sat in our driveway for the whole summer while he made do with another car. Finally, I took it back to the dealership and requested its repair or resale to another party. To date, nothing has been done. And I have not pursued it beyond an occasional phone call to mildly ask for a progress report. How long ago did I return the van to them? It will be two years come the end of summer.

And what I am now seeing is that this ridiculous behavior is all tied up with who I am as a compulsive overeater. It's not just my *eating* that is hostage to my disease, it's my whole *life;* and "unmanageable" is certainly not too strong a word to describe the net effect.

But I am starting to work on it. I suspect that progress will be strongly related to the development of more faith—that is, less dependence on Eliot's game plan for his life and for the rest of the world; and more trust in people who understand me and my disease, a program that obviously works for people who follow it, and a "Higher Power" who is really in charge.

I should say a word about this Higher Power business. It is

clear that OA is deeply rooted in faith. Not *a* faith, not a religion—not at all. Faith. Faith that somewhere outside ourselves is a Power that can be relied on to do for us what we cannot do for ourselves.

Some OA members regard the group itself as their Higher Power, while others talk of God "as we understand God." There is absolutely no effort by OA to get anybody to believe anything about any God or religion—only to be consistent about the conviction that we do not have within ourselves the power to run the world, to make happen all the things we've tried to make happen, even to manage what we would eat on any given day.

In other words, belief in our own powerlessness simply and obviously requires belief that there is real power somewhere else. The alternative is despair.

April 28

This is not the best of days for me. We spent the weekend visiting our oldest daughter at the college she attends. Her birthday and our wedding anniversary are five days apart, so we celebrated both all weekend long. I thought I was well-prepared to maintain my abstinence.

I was wrong.

Saturday night, we went to a terrific restaurant near her school. I do not have any trouble with restaurants, for the most part, because my constant business travels require me to eat out eight to ten meals a week. I have become quite careful about ordering and, in fact, frequently do not even look at the menu. I just say, "I'd like six ounces of broiled swordfish, a baked potato, green salad with oil and vinegar on the side" or whatever. I have discovered that almost any restaurant will prepare exactly what you ask for, whether it is on the menu or not. People respond to an honest declaration of need and are sympathetic when I say I am on a strict eating regimen.

So I ordered an abstinent meal at this place: broiled breast of chicken, four ounces of pasta, a salad. I was doing fine.

Until dessert.

I didn't order a dessert, but when the others' desserts came there was much oohing and aahing about them. And then: "Here, Eliot, you *must* have just a tiny taste of this."

Well, that sounded reasonable to me. Just a tiny taste. And, in truth, that is all I took.

When I told Andrew, he became very stern and declared, "You have broken your abstinence. What's the matter with you? Don't you know this disease can *kill* you?"

I tried to make light of the incident. After all, I said, it's not like I went on a binge and gobbled my way through a quart of ice cream and a package of Oreos or something.

He went berserk. (Quietly. Andrew is not a screamer. He just gets *intense*.) "That's worse, what you did. What you did is actually worse than a binge, because it implies that you think you can *control* this stuff, can control yourself. And *that's* what's fatal about it, thinking you can handle it. You've got a whole lifetime of failure behind you to prove you can't handle it, and then you sit there at the table and act like you can. Who do you think you're kidding, anyhow?"

He said he thought I had better give some real consideration to how serious I was about this program, because he had his doubts.

I understand Andrew's point and I respect it. In fact, my guess is that falling completely away from this program—if I ever were to—would come in tiny steps, so small I'd hardly notice them. No big falling-off-the-wagon binge. Just a gradual erosion of discipline and commitment, like the way a diet peters out toward the end when you start with a little of this and a little of that until, almost without noticing the crossing of a boundary, you're totally back to where you were before.

So today is Day One of my new abstinence. I hope the string lasts longer than the couple of months I got out of the first one.

May 17

My abstinence is steady now, and my appreciation for this program keeps growing and growing. I just got back from a meeting, and some of the stuff under discussion really struck home for me. Principally: honesty.

I'm beginning to understand that this program is not about food at all. It's about honesty. What I hear in these meetings is people—including me—coming clean about who they *really* are. I hear people—and feel myself—laying down the heavy burden of cover-up. I know my dishonesty with food brought me here, but I will stay here because of the joy I am getting from becoming honest in other areas of my life.

My eating has been a lifelong exercise in dishonesty, of course. Among the most deeply moving aspects of the OA experience for me is the way group members not only accept but applaud coming clean about that dishonesty. They have a saying that says it all: We are only as sick as our secrets. We all know honesty about food is the only basis for recovery.

But so is a fresh honesty in other parts of my life, parts that have also been full of pretense. I have lived in fear of ever being honest about my limits and shortcomings. I never knew it was all right to *have* limits and shortcomings. Can you imagine that? I continually tried to cover up the fact that there was anything I did not know or could not understand or was not able to master.

Back when I thought I was supposed to know everything already and be able to do everything, I had only two choices: I could pretend I knew what I was talking about and begin the difficult task of defending an ignorant point of view; or I could tackle the equally difficult task of wrestling the discussion around to a subject I did know something about.

What this cost me, in addition to chronic stress, was the chance to learn something new.

Now I almost revel in my newfound freedom to declare, "I don't know anything about that yet. Would you help me out, please?" Or "I don't understand. Could you please explain?" Or "I'm afraid that is beyond my abilities. You'll have to ask someone else to handle it."

Imagine! For forty years, I never felt free to say those simple sentences. What madness! And yet such was the daily burden of my life, trying to hide the fact that I was not on top of absolutely everything.

Do I now suddenly claim to be a completely honest person? Of course not. But I have gladly given up the impossible and corrupt goal of persuading myself and all others that I am something more than I am. Total honesty is my goal, if not my accomplishment, and it is the standard by which I'd like to measure my health every day. When I find myself drifting off into little dishonesties (like deciding not to weigh or measure food) or trying to exaggerate my importance in social or professional relationships, I can sense that I am in danger of losing what I have gained. My integrity and self-respect are at stake here, not to mention my very life.

May 26

Things are going pretty well again. I am back up to a month of abstinence and last time I weighed had lost seven more pounds. How far I have come, I suddenly realize, from the big plans I had in mind a year ago when I began this painful experiment, of being the "one in twenty" who could win at this game. I was out to wrestle this monster to earth and slay it with my own two hands back then—against long-shot odds. And guess what? The monster slew me instead; yet, ironically, now the odds are in my favor.

I guess this is what the word *paradox* means—getting the results you want by doing just the opposite of what you are inclined to do. You keep your kids only if you let them go. You regain control of a skidding car only if you take your foot *off* the brake and steer *toward* the danger. And you gain power over compulsive overeating and food only when you have been overpowered and beaten by them—and know it. Eliot, meet Paradox. You two are going to get along fine together.

The meeting topic today brought me up short as well. We were reading material on Step Seven, a Step about humility. In the middle of the chapter was a line that absolutely stunned me: "We have been demanding more than our share of security, prestige, and romance."*

What do they mean, "more than our share"!? I always thought the whole point was to get everything you could. Not by hook or by crook—I don't mean that. And not by unlimited greed either. I mean, I just thought that a bright and energetic person was supposed to, well, grow up to be President. Failing that, to pile up lots of money and goods and

---

Twelve Steps and Twelve Traditions (New York: A.A. World Services, Inc., 1985), 71. Reprinted with permission of A.A. World Services Inc.

recognition and happiness. Actually, it wasn't "lots"; it was to pile up *all you wanted.*

Now that's a very different idea. Because the horizon keeps stretching—and has kept stretching me out with it. How much did I want? More. That's all. That's the only measure. Just *more.* Like with food, too much was never enough.

I guess I thought my mission was to outcompete everybody. Never mind the big stuff—being president of the company or enjoying the things a sizeable salary can buy or even winning the tennis tournament. Nobody is embarrassed to confess to those kinds of competitive urges. But my competitiveness was constant and endless. How certifiably crazy: Did that jerk pass me on the highway? How can I slip past him again so that he'll know I edged him out without my wife knowing that I'm acting so juvenile? Or even so trivial a thing as walking up to a ticket booth with a friend— somehow, I would always angle to arrive ahead of him, to get mine first and be in a position of control.

Who knows where all that came from. I don't—and I don't care. All I care about is that this madness, too, could be lifted from me. I want to do well what is expected and required of me, but I don't want to be driven to do it better than someone else. I want it to be enough that I do it as well as I can, without concern for how well anyone else does it.

But I am looking for a better sense of when it is appropriate to turn on my competitiveness—to stay alive in business, for example—and when to let it lie quiet.

I find myself deeply wanting to believe that I am not intended to keep churning on an endless treadmill of competition and achievement, reaching ever higher and wider until I possess everything—except myself.

I see now that my grasping for all the world, my trying to make myself seem more important than I am, my trying to control people and events around me—all kept me from paying attention to the one thing that matters most: knowing and loving and living comfortably with myself.

I'd like my goals and expectations to be more modest now. Self-possession is my strongest desire, and I am trying to let self-possession determine *whether* I do something or not, and *how* I do it. This is not easy.

I face tough questions. Does giving up "more than [my] share of security, prestige, and romance" mean reducing my income? Selling our big house or our other beloved possessions? I do not know the answer to that as I write. I do know that I am quietly and calmly open to following the question wherever it leads.

And I know the answer will lead me somewhere I never planned to go. Thank God.

June 20

My life is truly changing. In fact, I can say that it has changed. *I* have changed. As my abstinence continues intact and excess weight continues to melt away, I feel a deep relaxation that goes right to the core of my being.

I believe I am feeling the departure of fear.

It is clear to me now how much of my life was driven by fears—of imperfection, of failure, of being found out. Especially of being found out. When I was both a sneaky compulsive overeater in private and a fake who pretended to know everything in public, let's face it, I had a lot to be found out about. You can't carry on that kind of deception without being constantly terrified deep inside, waiting to be exposed at any second as the private slob and public phony you're sure you are.

So I lived in fear—and buried my head. I was the ostrich of the century. Whatever it was, I just didn't want to know. I didn't want to know how much money was left in the checking account. I didn't want to know if someone was angry at me. I didn't want to know whether a piece of work I had done was all right.

I am simply amazed now at how carefully I avoided getting honest feedback from the world. It was as if I surrounded myself with filters that screened out anything negative headed my way. I really did *not* want to know. I must have been certain that I would be unable to face the truth and deal with it. Now, I know that nothing is as painful as being numb.

I'll be the first to admit that this ostrich isn't yet an eagle — and may never be. A friendlier, more realistic image might be that of the robin—attentive, alert, industrious, a harbinger of springtime. I'm none of those yet, but I do have my head out of the sand, I'm looking around, and I know that I am headed toward the summer of my life, not the winter. I am asking some questions, and I am listening to the answers.

I don't always like what I hear. But I love hearing *reality*. I won't hear anything I cannot cope with, and I will hear some things that will help me live more usefully.

And that is why I am now fear-less. The hyphen is important. Not "fearless," as in having no fears at all—not fear-free. I have less fear, not none. But I know that even the remaining fears, too, can be lifted.

That is why I also did not say "courageous." Courage is something, I think, one summons in the face of real danger. And the truth is, I don't think I face any dangers anymore.

I mean, what can hurt me? I could lose a lot: my business, my income, my homes, and all that. But I would not be

damaged. I could suffer unthinkable personal losses: the dis-
ability or death of a loved one. But again, though I would
suffer pain beyond anything I have yet experienced or can
even begin to imagine, I am not fearful. I am free of my lifelong sense of obligation to keep everything perfect and free
of pain for myself and others.

It is not up to me. I will take what comes.

August 1

Every time I go to an OA meeting, I learn more—and grow
more. I am astonished to see how inadequately I have lived.
But I am not ashamed. I am experiencing one of The Promises: "We will not regret the past nor wish to shut the door
on it." But I *do* wince a bit.

I see now how often I abused the people in my life. I did everything I could (in a sneaky way, to be sure) to control
them, to make decisions for them, to fit them into my view of
the way things should be. And when my sneaky manipulating didn't work, I resorted to a kind of semipolite bullying. I
was the one who determined how the house would be remodelled. I was the one who decided how the kitchen would
be organized. I was the one who sold my wife's beloved car
and foisted my old one on her, so I could get the new convertible I wanted.

Slowly, I am beginning to recognize the many, many ways in
which I have failed to respond to the needs and rights of
those around me. It is difficult and painful to face the way I
have behaved. But as I continue to take inventory, I find myself surprisingly willing to step forward and hold myself ac-
countable for my past behavior. I also find myself
surprisingly willing to renounce it as a pattern for the
future—willing, but not yet fully able. With a half-century of

momentum behind them, these habits are not easy to break. But I'm working on them.

One thing I have to work on is my willingness to share control—or even give up control. I have rarely liked following anybody else's lead. I was usually quite certain that their ideas or decisions were not going to be as good as mine.

My superman style of management of the universe has been built on a huge (and nutty) assumption: that everything was controllable and should be arranged to fall neatly into whatever pattern I carried in my head. My life was riddled with so many nuisances that didn't conform to my notion of the way they were supposed to be. These ranged from the kind of car my wife drove, to the colleges my children attended, to the way police were directing traffic, to the telephone wire that stretches across the view of the ocean from our vacation cottage. I see all this now as part of the grandiosity and control stuff. And as a distinct absence of humility and trust.

Imagine my surprise, then, to find myself recently on a "package tour" and *liking* it. Following a schedule others in the group had mapped out. Staying in hotels I might not have selected. Riding in a bus, of all things, as a mere passenger!

Does that mean I now seek to be just a face in the crowd? I doubt that. But it does seem to mean that I don't mind being led and putting myself in the care of others sometimes. There is simply no good reason for resisting chances to enjoy the relaxation that comes when I am not in charge. Relying on others really is a pretty good feeling.

Now, all I have to do is make sure that I don't poison the process by my lifelong habit of blaming other people when I don't get everything I want. I have lived a lot of my life in a foul mood, equal parts anger and melancholy. Anger at the people I was trying to please. Anger at the weight of responsibility for being a good provider. Anger at whatever was making me do something I didn't want to—even when I was unsure about what I *did* want.

The melancholy was a constant dreaming about the life I was not leading, the daylong daydream of how it should have been. If only. If only I had been born to wealth. If only I had more courage. If only I didn't have such high principles. If only I could spend more time writing. If only I had the metabolism of my brothers; they can eat anything they want and never gain a pound. *If only I were not fat!*

But the uncomfortable truth is that most of my circumstances are of my own making. They are the overall effect of decades of decisions I have made consciously and unconsciously, of actions I took and actions I failed to take. They are what really brought me to where I am. And the rest is just, you know, just life, as it happens.

I am ready to own my lifetime of decisions and to own the effect of them. I have had a rich and fulfilling life despite my painful disease and some defects of character I find regrettable. I am satisfied to be who I have become, and I have stopped dreaming about what never was and can never be.

Now, I just pray for the willingness to continue to change.

October 20

Although I am maintaining my abstinence and continuing to lose weight, I can't get interested in writing about that anymore. So much else is happening for me in this program, the weight seems irrelevant.

What matters most is the continuing change in my outlook

on life. I find myself moving gracefully toward a sense of balance that is close to bliss. And with the movement, I am watching a lifetime of resentment drift away.

I recall how I resented thin people. All my life, I have felt their barbs, stinging me with the truth about myself I hated beyond all bounds. But so, too, have I resented anybody else who judged me in any way. Or who had something I did not have. Or who was born into money and privilege and possibilities that were beyond my reach.

For the most part, though, I did not express my resentment openly; just the opposite. I did everything I could to get friendly with them. I see now that I was chasing a kind of fairy-godmother fantasy that somehow, somewhere, a magical transfusion would come from them to me and make me all right at last.

All that is over for me now. I know that I have no way to benefit from living in a dream world. I have in my world, and in myself, all the richness I could ever ask for and more than I will ever fully appreciate. Just having the opportunity to sit here this morning and feel what I am feeling, think what I am thinking, write what I am writing—that's my rightful treasure.

It is enough.

January 15

Tonight, I led the meeting for the first time. The experience solidified my thinking about myself as a member of OA. While I have certainly considered myself seriously committed to this organization for a long time now, nothing can ever quite say "I belong here" like *qualifying*—spending half an hour telling a roomful of your fellow members the truth about your life as a compulsive overeater.

I showed them the portraits that Pat Hamm did. I now resemble the "as desired" version of Eliot far more than the "as was" since I have now lost over forty pounds and my abstinence now exceeds 250 consecutive days. I shared that I have a totally new wardrobe and that I *loved* shopping for clothes—for the first time in my life. I got rid of my oversized old clothes, rather than keeping them "just in case," because I believe I will never, ever compulsively overeat again in my life—God willing.

I went on to talk about other changes, deeper changes, in my life. With good reason, I introduced my "spiritual" experience somewhat hesitantly. Nothing is more personal than religious/spiritual life, and I did not want to invade anyone's privacy with my own experience. From the earliest founding of Alcoholics Anonymous to the adoption of the AA program by OA, members have been careful not to promote or impose any particular belief system on newcomers. They have also been careful not to scare off prospective members by suggesting that the program would ever require them to buy into a religious life or mind-set they might object to.

That is why I, too, tiptoed into this territory. But tiptoe or not, I had to speak about it; to have remained silent would be both dishonest about my own transformation and misleading about the source of the power that enables my recovery. Even now, reflecting about it, I marvel at the contrast between before and after.

"Before" I can summarize with a snapshot or two. I grew up paying more attention to the religious part of my life than most people, I think. As a kid, I went to church when my parents didn't, and in college I took part in religious organizations. I cared enough about finding the right faith for myself that I quit the church I grew up in and made a fairly radical switch. Later, I studied at a theological seminary for three years, taught theology and ethics at a college, and served as a parish minister.

None of this, however, made it any easier for me to get in tune with the spiritual dimension of OA than it is for anybody else. Why? First, my formal training in theology tended to make me suspicious of the "informal" spirituality of a group like OA. I had seen too many oddball religious sects manipulating too many gullible members over the years.

The second reason, though, is far more important. The truth is that I never relied on the God of my formal training at all. I *talked* about that God a good deal, of course. And I had some wonderful experiences in worship and in the church community.

But for all of my life prior to OA, I *relied* on myself. When push came to shove, I counted on Eliot to set my directions, Eliot to provide everything my family and I needed, Eliot to solve whatever problems I had in life. I guess I believed that I had enough willpower to take care of everything and everybody.

We all know, of course, how that turned out. Relying on my own willpower was taking the fast lane to an early death—without ever having really lived. I dwelled in a living death called despair.

Despair is truly hell, and lately, I began to wonder why despair so frequently befell me as I failed in my efforts to control my eating. Suddenly it was so obvious: if I am the highest power in my life and I have demonstrated beyond a doubt that I do not have enough power to beat this compulsive overeating, then there is simply no way to deal with my disease. No way whatsoever. The situation is totally hopeless and I am good as dead.

It doesn't get much more basic than that.

And so, when I finally recognized my powerlessness over food, I had only two choices: despair about my powerlessness, or dependence on some Power higher than myself to help me escape my despair and the living death that was too soon to become my physical death.

Thus my faith was born. And thus it continues day by day, as I actively seek and eagerly rely on the Higher Power in my life. While I still use much of the religious language and many of the concepts of faith I learned earlier in life, it is all different for me now. I used to know the words; now I know what they *mean*. And I know what they mean for *me*.

Once the subject of my work, my faith is now the source of my life.

EPILOGUE

For today, I am still abstinent.

Nearly four years have passed since I wrote the preceding pages. I might have tried to get them printed back then, in hopes of sharing my wonderful "discovery" with the world. Yet I feared to do that. There was still the chance, however remote it felt, that this was just one more disappointment-in-the-making for myself and for fat people everywhere. I needed to know that the gains in my personal life and the losses in my physical bulk were real—and permanent.

They are.

One day at a time, that is. For today, I am still abstinent. I have over fifteen hundred consecutive days of abstinence since the tasting of the desserts. I have maintained a fifty-pound weight loss for nearly three years now. (Without OA, I would now weigh between 250 and 300—assuming I weren't dead of a heart attack or stroke; instead, I weigh 172 to 174.) My blood pressure is now completely normal, well below danger zones without any medication (I went off the beta-blocker drugs over four years ago).

I have been to at least one OA meeting every week during that period, and I have called my sponsor to commit my food nearly every day as well.

After a lifetime of confusion, I now know that I am neither a fat person nor a slender person. I am a compulsive overeater who will either be fat or slender depending on how I deal with my disease, one day at a time. For today, I am O.K.

Overeating, I now know, wasn't the only way I could behave compulsively, just the most deadly. Lately, I have been discovering old habits that reveal I have been compulsive for a long time. And unfortunately, I have also invented new ways to exercise the compulsive energies no longer spent on overeating.

The long-time habits that I now recognize as compulsive behavior range from a persistent determination to close doors and cap toothpaste tubes and straighten crooked pictures, to an almost comical incident just last week. We had a few people over for dinner, and at the conclusion of the main course, I happened to notice the way scraps were arrayed on people's plates. The others' plates were littered with the usual helter-skelter jumble of discards. But mine? I saw that I had taken the six tails from the six shrimp I had eaten and laid each one in perfect alignment with the others, like a little pink picket fence.

Then, ringed all around the rim of my plate, lay my entire array of artichoke leaves all nested precisely within each other as though fitted in place by a Swiss watchmaker.

More gravely, though, I gradually realized that during my second year of abstinence—my second year of not permitting my deep compulsivity to express itself through overeating—I went on a binge of spending money. In a little over six months, I acquired an expensive new car, an expensive new boat, numerous accessories and gadgets for the boat, a living room full of expensive antiques and carpets, and all sorts of electronic consumer products. In addition, we extensively remodelled both our residence and our summer cottage, travelled to the Middle East, staged two multithousand-dollar parties, and totally relandscaped our yard.

That binge is over, thank God. But it served as a grim warning to me that I am coping with a very powerful force that will seize control of my judgment and behavior at any opportunity. Only day-by-day dedication to my process of recovery will hold my compulsive behavior in check.

I am doing my best, but I need a lot of help.

Back on the positive-benefits side (which is, by light years, the larger, stronger side): I have enjoyed clarifying my relationships with the people in my life. When I was buried in compulsive overeating, I lived out a silently negotiated, one-sided contract with those around me. I would do whatever I had to do to avoid making them irritated with me. Why? I wanted to avoid creating any occasion on which, in their irritation, they might turn on me and criticize my eating behavior and my fatness. I know that sounds weird, but it is absolutely true, I am sure. I felt so ashamed and so vulnerable because of my not-so-secret vice that I never felt the right to really stand up to touchy issues. All I wanted to do was keep everybody happy—and off my case.

Trying to keep everybody happy is a fairly tough job, chiefly because it is impossible. But tackling the impossible seemed preferable to running the risk of being stabbed with the truth about my compulsive overeating, and so I paid the price.

I don't do that anymore. I know the truth about myself, and I accept myself for the flawed, pretty ordinary guy I am. I don't expect to be any more of a person than I am. And I refuse to let others expect more of me than is reasonable. If someone is critical of me, they may well be right—I don't need to deny my shortcomings. I just do the best I can, that's all. And that is good enough.

And so *I am not ashamed about anything anymore,* which means I do not fear others' demands or attacks. (Imagine that! It feels incredible!)

I am also learning that, along with my not being all-powerful and not being in control, I am not able to make everybody happy. That is not my responsibility. What *is* my responsibility is to see that Eliot lives the modest and purposeful life he was born to live. Naturally, I want to do that as cooperatively and pleasantly with my loved ones and friends and colleagues as I possibly can. But if I occasionally have to sacrifice harmony in order to stand up for myself, I'd rather pay that price now. It is a one-time cost, not an endless burden of installments.

These and other changes in my life are so deep and important as to be almost indescribable. It would take another book to do them justice. Let me just say that the deep gift of serenity has continued as a blessing I treasure every day. So has the gift of faith and trust, the willingness to listen to others and to share control, the determination to trust the truth and rely on honesty to prevail in *every* matter.

Perhaps the best way to sum up the change in my life is this: *I have renounced my audience.*

Audience? What audience?

The audience I have been playing to for my whole life. The audience I carry in my head that sets an agenda of achievement, and then rewards me with hollow "attaboys" when I win, and condemns me with sour disapproval when I fail to attain *everything* that others have attained.

I finally recognized that I was playing to an audience three years ago when, after my spending binge, I "had it all." What more could anyone ask? We owned all this expensive stuff, we lived this Good Life, we made some donations, we put on a couple of spectacular parties. All told, we spent an awesome amount of money in conspicuous and not-so-conspicuous ways. What more *could* anyone ask?

More. Just more. And more and more and more. Suddenly the truth was clear: too much would never be enough. At the height of my prosperity, I was still in a kind of bankruptcy. My striving was not being motivated by a desire to achieve, but by a competitive envy, striving to show my audience that I finally belonged on the winner's stand.

Stunned, I realized that the thrill really *is* in the chase, not in the having—but that the audience wanted me to chase on *forever*. This is a brutal audience, chanting for blood, incapable of being satisfied. The harder I run, the more it demands. The more I have, the less impressed it is. At last, I came to understand the words of Janis Joplin, the sixties rock singer who rose to stardom in a frenzy of performing energy and died of a drug overdose: what the audience really wants deep down, she said, is to see you kill yourself before their eyes on stage.

Her audience, at least, was real. Mine, thank God, is not. But it has taken me, regrettably, fifty-one years to understand that mine is but a phantom, the ghosts and echoes of earlier days. Sure, there were real people watching and judging when I was younger—parents, teachers, schoolmates, employers, and all the rest. But they are long gone. For a good fifteen or twenty years now, the seats have been empty—but I have carried on as though there was a jury sitting out there turning thumbs up or thumbs down, life-giving or death-dealing. What a hoax I have played on myself all these years. *Nobody is watching now. Nobody cares whether I make it or not.* So it is time to change.

My early audience imprinted strong messages on me and I cannot erase them. But I can certainly look at them differently at this stage of my life and experience. Yes, I have enjoyed being a good provider; that gave me a lot of fulfillment. But I can renounce the vain ambition of being a hero-father to my children; I cannot possibly fulfill my own fantasies for that role—and they don't need me to do anything for them anyhow. Better for them to achieve what they will on their own at this point.

And, yes, I have enjoyed having "the things money can buy"; I would rather have antique furniture and new cars than the other way around. As a fifties teenager in California, the highest good was dragging the Main in an eye-catching car; even today, traces of that juvenile dream bubble up in me the first weeks after pulling out of an automobile showroom.

But I am increasingly mindful of what the great Indian leader

Mohandas K. Gandi said: "He who has more than he needs is a thief."

I still enjoy the thrill of competing for an important new piece of business—and winning. The work we do is highly worthwhile and we do it uncommonly well. The report card from our clients is gratifying. But they are the audience only for my work, not for my *life*. And I am learning, at long last, how profoundly different the two are. My work would become my whole life, were I to commit myself forever to the sixty- to seventy-hour weeks that are standard in our business.

Yet nobody ever said on his or her deathbed, "I wish I had spent more time at the office."

And so I decided to spend less time at the office. Or, more accurately, I decided to spend more time at my life beyond the office. I wanted more time to feel, to think, to write, to read, to explore the deeper dimensions of my personal development and my spiritual life. At the beginning of this past year, then, I reclaimed 25 percent of my work time—one full week off every month—for these personal pursuits. That time is spent doing exactly what I am doing now: writing, thinking, feeling, traveling, talking, listening. Living. I am in ecstasy during these moments, and I know I am living the life I was born to live.

There has been a cost, of course: in return for this freedom, I took a 25 percent decrease in my income. I also relinquished my role as co-chief executive officer of the firm and turned over total control of the company to my co-founding partner.

Because it may sound as though I had been doing O.K., one might conclude that all this was fairly easy to do—just a well-off guy deciding to coast securely on past gains. Quite the contrary. This has been a powerfully painful readjustment for me. It has been the *right* thing to do, for certain. But astonishingly difficult.

For one thing, our household budget didn't have anything like a 25 percent margin of income over expenses. Like many others, I suspect, we had been spending pretty much everything that came in; over time, we had built up fixed expenses and spending patterns that left little to save or invest. (Investment for retirement? I had always imagined that in the next few years, after this heavy-duty tuition-paying was over, we'd have the big margin for building up our "security.") So the sudden 25 percent whack in income meant something big had to give.

In tears of deep, deep pain, we eventually concluded we must part with our beloved Maine cottage, for ten years the scene of the most cherished moments in our family life— summertime frolics and Thanksgiving weeks and family weddings and soul-restoring moments of quietly watching the ocean breaking on the rocks below. This was the place, I dreamed, where generations to come would find their family history, the place where my wife and I would reign as genial grandparents for decades.

And now, suddenly, it is gone.

I can say truthfully that letting go of that place was the most painful voluntary decision I have ever made. The boat, too, had to go. The new owners took possession of everything in August. But, beyond the loss of the cottage and the boat, I was also relinquishing the fantasy of myself as family hero, as the "good provider" who could fulfill my own and everyone else's dreams about what a man like me should be able to do for his loved ones. It has been hell.

And all for what? Why was I doing this, anyhow? Wasn't this

just a self-indulgence, or worse, midlife irresponsibility masquerading as a search for a truer self? Was I hiding a garden-variety burnout behind noble-sounding motives? Couldn't I just keep on keeping on for a few more years? Wasn't there an easier, softer way to change my life?

Not that I could find.

Naturally, I'd rather have held onto a bigger income and all those possessions. I am not stupid. And I am not a lover of hardship. I prefer living in our big house and driving our fine cars than not. But I cannot have it all; there are trade-offs in life. And I simply cannot hold back the tidal wave of my own development, a wave that is sweeping me onto shores of unexplored territory. I have no doubt that future change will require additional adjustments, letting go of more and more of what I worked hard to achieve and had come to treasure. These adjustments are hard and the timing couldn't be worse.

But is it ever good? Not if a person is really open to a different life, and I am.

I am now listening for a voice other than my own, too long the overly obedient echo of the phantom audience. I am trying to live one day at a time, modestly and responsively, instead of grandly and aggressively. I am doing my best to rely less on my financial striving and more on my faith.

This gift of faith has been the finest gift of these years of change. I know now how different faith is from "belief." Beliefs can and do change. But what I have been given is *knowledge* of God's presence and guidance in my life. It is real. It is a fact. And you don't change facts; they change you.

So now I *know* that we were created on purpose and live in God's garden. We are not an accident of chemistry or physics. God wanted us here, the way we are. I don't have to "believe in" this; I have experienced this fact and need only to remember and trust it. And *use* it. So far, I have never failed to detect God's will for me at any moment if I sought it, listened for it, and really welcomed it.

I am on a different path now, playing out my life more modestly among loving family and friends whom I can regard as supportive companions, not an audience to impress. If I have an audience at all anymore, it is God; from here on I am playing for an audience of one.

My experience was predicted and described, in fact, in The Promises I heard in one of those first OA meetings: I *do* know a new freedom and a new happiness. I do not regret the past nor wish to shut the door on it. I truly comprehend the word *serenity* and know peace. I can see how my experience can benefit others. And my feelings of uselessness and self-pity have disappeared. I am losing interest in selfish things and gaining interest in other people. Self-seeking is slipping away. My whole attitude and outlook on life has changed. Fear of people and economic insecurity has left me. I know how to handle situations that used to baffle me. And I realize that God is doing for me what I could not do for myself.

Those who know me and love me say I am a different man.

They are right.